BLAST OFF!

on
New York
Science

Book 4

Buckle Down
PUBLISHING COMPANY

Acknowledgments:

The science editors gratefully acknowledge the author team of James A. Shymansky, Larry D. Yore, Michael P. Clough, John A. Craven III, Sandra K. Enger, Laura Henriques, Tracy M. Hogan, Leigh Monhardt, Rebecca M. Monhardt, Jo Anne Ollerenshaw, John W. Tillotson, and Peter Veronesi.

Elementary Learning Standards from the University of the State of New York, the State Education Department. Used with permission.

Every effort has been made by the publisher to locate each owner of the copyrighted material reprinted in this publication and to secure the necessary permissions. If there are any questions regarding the use of these materials, the publisher will take appropriate corrective measures to acknowledge ownership in future publications.

ISBN 0-7836-2138-8

Catalog #BF NY4S 1

6 7 8 9 10

President and Publisher: Douglas J. Paul, Ph.D.; Editorial Director: John Hansen; Science Editor: Jennifer R. Horn Brown; Editorial Assistant: Molly Hansen; Production Editor: Michael Hankes; Production Director: Jennifer Booth; Art Director: Chris Wolf; Graphic Designer: Kim Dutton.

Cover image: © Corbis/Digital Stock

TABLE OF CONTENTS

UNIT 1

Scientific Inquiry

Scientific Inquiry

From the time you wake up in the morning until you go to sleep at night, you are asking questions and solving problems—in other words, you are inquiring. Science is about **inquiry**. A good scientist is a good inquirer.

What Do You Think?

Have you ever been given a riddle to solve? The answers are usually pretty simple, but they can be tricky to figure out. Try to answer this riddle:

1. Clue 1: I have teeth, but I do not bite.

   Clue 2: I have a blade, but I do not fight.

   Clue 3: I cut through wood, but I'm not a termite.

   What am I?_____

2. Explain how each clue helped you solve the riddle.

   Clue 1: _____

   Clue 2: _____

   Clue 3: _____

Key Words

experiment

hypothesis

inquiry

scientific method

variable

What People Think

If you ask scientists to explain how they do their work, they will probably tell you about the **scientific method**. They might make the scientific method sound like using a recipe to bake a cake.

3. What are you supposed to do when you use a recipe to make something?

_____

Unlike baking a cake, though, there are no step-by-step recipes for doing science. This means that *there is no one scientific method.* Each new problem or question may be different from an earlier one. So you have to be like a creative cook and make up your own recipe for each new problem. For example, what if you had some chocolate brownie mix but no recipe for making brownies?

4. Suppose you have several boxes of the same kind of brownie mix, but no directions. You know that you have to add either a cup of milk or a cup of water to the mix. How can you solve this problem "scientifically" and without asking anyone for help?

_____

_____

_____

Because there are no step-by-step recipes for science, inquiry skills are very important to scientists. One thing, however, is certain: Science starts with questions. Suppose, for example, that you want to grow the largest possible tomato. Your first question could be, *What will help a tomato plant grow the largest tomatoes?* Let's plan an **experiment** that will help you figure out what will make tomatoes grow bigger.

To start, you could make a good guess about what will help the tomatoes grow bigger. A good guess is called a **hypothesis**.

5. Write a hypothesis about one thing that could help tomatoes grow bigger.

_____

_____

You know that plants need sun and water to grow. Gardeners and farmers often use fertilizer to help plants grow, too. Let's suppose that you are going to test how fertilizer helps tomato plants. Let's say that your hypothesis is this: Adding fertilizer to the soil around a tomato plant will help the plant produce bigger tomatoes.

There are many **variables**, or things that can change, when you grow tomato plants. For example, the plants could get different amounts of water or sunlight, be grown in a pot or in the ground, or get different amounts of fertilizer. If an experiment is to be a fair test, *you must allow only one variable to change in the test.*

6. You are testing the hypothesis that adding fertilizer to the soil helps tomato plants produce bigger tomatoes. Which of these variables should you change?
    A. the amount of water each plant gets
    B. the amount of sunlight each plant gets
    C. whether the plants get fertilizer or not
    D. whether the plants are grown in pots or in the ground

7. Should you grow some tomato plants without any fertilizer for this experiment?
    A. No, so that you can be sure that the fertilizer helped.
    B. Yes, so that you don't have to buy as much fertilizer.
    C. No, because the purpose of the experiment is to grow bigger tomatoes.
    D. Yes, because otherwise you wouldn't know whether using fertilizer made any difference.

8. Suppose that you grew eight tomato plants in the same garden. You put the same amount of fertilizer on four plants, and you didn't put any fertilizer on the other four plants. Everything else was kept the same (same amount of sunlight, water, and so on for each plant).

    Explain how you would decide whether your hypothesis (fertilizer helps tomato plants produce bigger tomatoes) was correct.

    _____

    _____

    _____

9. List the tools you would need to complete this experiment.

_____

_____

_____

_____

Practice Questions

1. Three fourth-graders want to find out which of their bicycles is the fastest at coasting down a hill. Which of the following would provide the most useful information?

    A. microscope and balance

    B. telescope and light meter

    C. meter stick and stopwatch

    D. barometer and thermometer

2. Four friends decide to see who can go the fastest on his or her skateboard. They pick a starting point, then put marks at 30 meters and at 60 meters. One at a time, they skate as fast as they can while two of the others time them. The table below shows the data they recorded.

Skateboard Times

	Time		
	At 30-meter mark	*At 60-meter mark*	
Amy	8 seconds	13 seconds	
Brock	7 seconds	11 seconds	
Colin	7 seconds	13 seconds	
Denzil	6 seconds	12 seconds	

Who was the fastest skateboarder for the 60-meter distance?

    A. Amy

    B. Brock

    C. Colin

    D. Denzil

3. Denzil claims that he was really the fastest skateboarder. Why might he feel that he was the fastest?

_____

_____

_____

_____

Directions: Use the following information to answer Numbers 4 and 5.

A fourth-grade class did an experiment to answer this question: How do things float in salt water compared to tap water?

They used these materials:

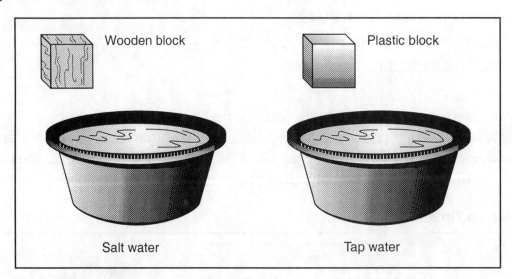

This is what they did:

- They filled two bowls with equal amounts of water. One bowl contained salt water, the other contained tap water.
- They floated a wooden block in the salt water.
- They floated a plastic block in the tap water.

This is what they found out: The plastic block floated higher in the tap water than the wooden block floated in the salt water.

4. What can the students conclude from this experiment?

  A. Plastic things cannot float in salt water.

  B. Plastic blocks float higher than wooden blocks.

  C. Things float higher in tap water than in salt water.

  D. This experiment doesn't answer their question.

5. Explain how you chose your answer to Number 4.

_____

_____

_____

_____

PEOPLE IN SCIENCE

Sara Josephine Baker
(United States 1873–1945)

When Sara Baker was growing up, she was inspired by her Aunt Abby. Abby was a Quaker[1] and a non-conformist[2] who questioned the way things were done in the nineteenth century. In the spirit of her aunt, Baker grew up to become a doctor at a time when few women reached that position. She was named a medical inspector for the New York City Department of Health, where she saw much poverty. She was shocked to find that more than 1,500 babies, most of whom came from poor families, died each week in the city. Baker refused to accept this tragic situation. She believed the key was in preventive medicine—preventing the conditions that caused infants' and young children's deaths. She was made the first chief of the Division of Child Hygiene[3] in New York City. By the time Baker retired, the infant death rate in N.Y.C. had been reduced by 66 percent. Baker saved thousands of lives by changing the way medicine treated its patients.

[1] Quaker: a member of the Quaker religion, which promotes peace and refuses to fight in wars
[2] non-conformist: a person who doesn't follow accepted patterns of thought and action
[3] hygiene: science that sets up and maintains health standards

Review 2

Collecting Data

How do scientists collect information? They do it the same way you do: They use their five **senses**. But are your five senses—sight, hearing, taste, touch, and smell—enough? In this review, you will find out more about making observations to solve problems.

What Do You Think?

To solve problems and make good decisions, you have to start with good information—what scientists call **data**.

1. For each of the following questions, describe how you could collect the necessary data.

    How far is it to your school? _____

    _____

    How much time does it take to walk to school? _____

    _____

    Who is the oldest person in your class? _____

    _____

    What was the loudest noise at school yesterday?

    _____

    _____

Key Words

data

data table

error

estimate

instrument

observation

precision

sense

Scientists also need to decide what data are important to collect. For example, what if a teacher wants to figure out which questions on the science test were easiest for the students to answer correctly? It probably wouldn't be very helpful to ask how many minutes each student spent studying for the test. Or what if a veterinarian wants to know how tall the average African elephant is? Measuring the distance between the ears won't be very helpful.

2. In order to find out how tall the average African elephant is, how should the veterinarian measure the elephants?

_____

_____

What People Think

You make an **observation** every time you notice something with one of your senses. For example, if you notice that the color of a pencil is yellow or a plate of food feels hot, you are making observations. Sometimes, when we need more information, we need to use special tools, or **instruments**, to make observations or measure things.

3. Name at least three measuring instruments.

_____

_____

Measurements are very important in science because they help scientists see patterns in data. But it is not always necessary to get exact data to find a pattern. Scientists often **estimate** measurements before making precise (as exact as possible) measurements. An estimate is a good guess about a measurement without actually measuring or calculating it. For example, you might estimate that a certain building is about three times as tall as your school building because your school has one floor and the other building has three floors.

4. How might you estimate the height of a tree in the park?

_____

_____

Estimates can give you an *idea* of how big, tall, or heavy something is. But to have **precision** in your measurements—to be as exact as possible—you need to use measuring tools. *Measurements are never exact, however.* There is always some amount of **error** (mistake) in any measurement. For example, if someone wanted to know how tall you are, you could stand against the wall, make a mark at the top of your head, and then measure the height with a meter stick. But the measurement would not be exact.

5. How could a mistake or error be made when measuring your height this way?

_____

_____

_____

One way to be more precise is to make more than one measurement. Several measurements can be averaged together to give a more precise measurement.

When researchers gather information, the data sometimes can be put into a table called a **data table**. The data table at the right shows information about how the fourth-grade students at Central Elementary School travel to school in the morning.

Form of Transportation	Number of Students
Bus	|||| ||||	
Car	|||
Bike	|||| ||||
Foot	|||| |||

6. How many students are in the class?

   A. 4
   B. 11
   C. 31
   D. 36

7. Which form of transportation is used by the most students?

   A. bus
   B. car
   C. bike
   D. foot

8. What fraction of the class walks to school?

   A. $\frac{8}{11}$

   B. $\frac{8}{31}$

   C. $\frac{11}{36}$

   D. 8

Practice Questions

Directions: Use the following illustration to answer Numbers 1 and 2. Each floor tile in the room is 30 cm wide and 30 cm long.

1. About how tall is the girl lying on the floor?

   A. 90 cm

   B. 105 cm

   C. 120 cm

   D. 135 cm

2. The boy in the picture is wondering how many marbles it would take to cover the whole floor in the classroom. He has only 100 or so. What could he do to estimate an answer?

   _____

   _____

   _____

Directions: Use the following information to answer Numbers 3 through 6.

Doug has a fish named Blinky. Blinky lives in a fish tank. Doug observed the temperature in his fish tank for five days. He recorded the temperatures in the table shown here.

Temperature in Blinky's Fish Tank

Day	Temperature
Monday	23°C
Tuesday	21°C
Wednesday	25°C
Thursday	24°C
Friday	26°C

3. Which sentence best describes the temperature of the water that Doug measured?

    A. The temperature goes up and down during the week.

    B. The temperature goes up a little bit each day of the week.

    C. The temperature goes down a little bit each day of the week.

    D. There is no temperature change during the week.

4. Which instrument should Doug use to find out if the depth of the water in the fish tank is the same each day?

    A.    B. 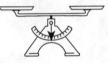   C. 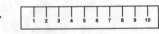   D.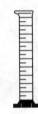

5. Doug feeds Blinky every day. Which instrument should Doug use to find out how much the food weighs?

    A.    B. 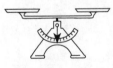   C. 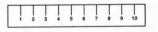   D.

6. This is a picture of Doug's fish Blinky. Make three observations about Blinky. Write your observations on the lines that follow.

_____

_____

_____

Review 3

Using Graphs

Have you ever heard the expression "A picture is worth a thousand words"? A **graph** is a way of representing numbers in picture form. Graphs make interpreting number information easier. They can help you communicate data you have collected in a scientific investigation. This review will give you practice using data in different kinds of graphs.

What Do You Think?

When you were born, you were probably somewhere around 20 inches long. You sure have grown a lot since then!

1. In the box below, create a graph that shows how your height has changed since you were born.

Key Words

bar graph

circle graph

graph

line graph

Your teacher will tell you how many students are in each grade in your school.

2. Write down the number of students in each grade in the table that follows.

Grade	Number of Students

3. Now create a graph that shows in picture form how many students are in each grade in your school. Try to make this graph different from the last one you made.

What People Think

When scientists interpret data, they look for patterns. Graphing the data makes those patterns easier to see.

There are three main types of graph: the **bar graph**, the **circle graph**, and the **line graph**.

A bar graph can be used to compare data that can be put into separate groups. In Review 2, you discussed how to research the ways students travel to school in the morning. A bar graph like the one shown here can be a good way to compare the groups of data in this kind of research.

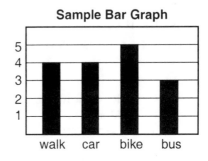

Sample Bar Graph

4. According to the sample bar graph, how many people take the bus?

    A. 3   C. 5

    B. 4   D. 16

A circle graph is used when you want to show how much of a whole a certain part represents. If you wanted to show the number of students who have brown eyes (a part) as a portion of your class (the whole), you would probably use a circle graph as shown here. Circle graphs also are called *pie charts*.

Sample Circle Graph

5. How many different eye colors are represented in the circle graph?

A line graph shows how data changes over time. If you were going to graph the high temperatures in a city for a certain period of time, you would probably use a line graph such as the one shown here.

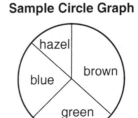

Sample Line Graph

6. According to the line graph, which is the hottest month of the year?

    A. May   C. July

    B. June   D. August

Practice Questions

Directions: Sehba and Kim were preparing a project for their science class. They collected weather data for one week. On the 15th of March, the class took a field trip, and the girls were unable to record any weather data except the sky conditions.

To share their information, they decided to make several graphs. Use their graphs to answer Numbers 1 through 5.

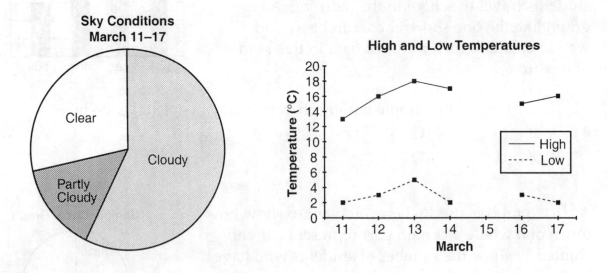

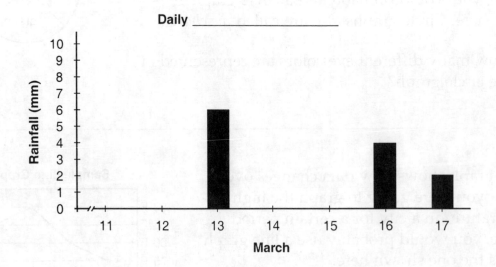

1. Which sentence best describes the pattern of temperatures Sehba and Kim measured?

    A. When highs got warmer, lows got colder.

    B. When highs got warmer, lows got warmer.

    C. The difference between highs and lows showed no pattern.

    D. The difference between highs and lows was the same each day.

2. Which word(s) would best complete the bar graph's title?

    A. Rainfall   C. Temperatures

    B. Cloud Cover   D. Clouds and Rainfall

3. What can you learn from the circle graph?

    A. Rain fell on more than half of the days.

    B. The skies were cloudy more than half of the days.

    C. The sun shone for some of each day during the week.

    D. The "partly cloudy" days were more cloudy than clear.

4. For each answer you did *not* choose in Number 3, explain why it is wrong.

    Answer letter _____ is wrong because _____

    _____

    Answer letter _____ is wrong because _____

    _____

    Answer letter _____ is wrong because _____

    _____

5. If Sehba and Kim had been able to record the temperature on March 15, which of the following would they most likely have recorded?

    A. High 4°C, Low 4°C

    B. High 16°C, Low 2°C

    C. High 30°C, Low 0°C

    D. High 13°C, Low 10°C

Review 4

Judging Ideas

Do you ever have to make choices about the games you and your friends play? One friend may want to play ball. Another friend may want to play computer games. Maybe you want to work on building a fort. So, you and your friends have to make a choice. When you make choices, you usually think about the problem. Then you decide what seems to be the best choice.

Science also is about picking the best choice. You will learn more about how science works in this review.

What Do You Think?

Both Alan and Tammi watched robins build nests for their science projects. In his report to the class, Alan said that robins repair and use old nests of other birds. Tammi, on the other hand, said that robins use grass, twigs, and paper scraps to build their nests new.

1. How would you decide which classmate to believe?

   _____

   _____

   _____

When a person makes a statement he or she wants us to believe is true, that statement is called a **claim**.

2. How do scientists decide whether to believe what another scientist claims?

   _____

   _____

   _____

Key Words

accurate

claim

evaluate

evidence

judgment

What People Think

Imagine two TV commercials: The makers of Fruitiest Fruit Juice claim that Fruitiest is the healthiest fruit juice you can buy, while the makers of SlurpyGood Fruit Juice claim that *it* is healthiest. Which fruit juice really is healthiest? We have to make **judgments** like these all the time. When you make a judgment, you decide what the best action or opinion is. It can be hard to decide what to do or what to believe.

3. If you are trying to judge which of two foods is healthiest for you to eat, what should you do to get information that will help you decide?

   A. Taste the foods.

   B. Look carefully at both foods.

   C. Check the magazine ads for the foods.

   D. Read the nutrition labels on the food packages.

Scientists also must make judgments when they are working. They make decisions based on the **evidence**, or clues, they have gathered. They make judgments based on what they have learned from past study, too. For example, suppose a scientist who is working in the jungle finds some tiny "strings" in her river water samples. She thinks that these tiny "strings" might actually be animals.

4. What kind of evidence or clues would you tell her to look for when deciding if the strings are some kind of animal?

   _____

   _____

   _____

Scientists need good evidence that they can count on in order to make the best choices. Scientists often use scientific instruments, or tools, to collect accurate observations and measurements. The tools might be as simple as a meter stick or as fancy as a robot.

5. What are some tools that the scientist working in the jungle could use to learn more about the "strings" and find out if they are animals?

_____

_____

_____

It is very important that the measurements a scientist uses are **accurate**. In other words, the measurements must be as exact as possible.

6. How could the scientist working in the jungle make sure her measurement of the length of the "strings" is accurate?

A. She could ask someone else to measure the "strings" for her.

B. She could measure the length several times; if the number is the same each time, she will know her measurement is accurate.

C. She could compare her measurements to the length of animals she thinks are similar; if the measurements are the same, she will know her measurement is accurate.

D. She could first guess how long the "strings" are and then measure with a scientific instrument; if her guess is the same as the measurement with the instrument, she will know her measurement is accurate.

As scientists collect evidence, they need to make sense of it and to decide what it means. Scientists must **evaluate** the information they gather before they make their decisions. They look at all of the evidence and decide whether their first idea still makes sense or whether they can find another answer to their question. In order for a choice to make sense, there must be data to support it. Any choices that are not backed by data are not good choices.

7. Suppose that after the scientist in the jungle has studied the "strings" more closely, she finds that they don't move or contain cells. Should she still claim that the "strings" are animals? Why or why not?

_____

_____

_____

Practice Questions

Directions: Use the pictures shown here to answer Numbers 1 and 2.

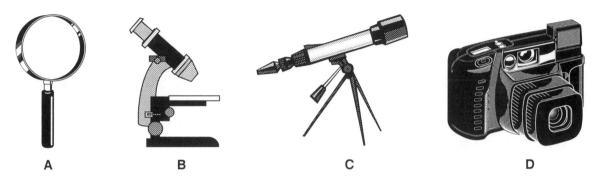

A	B	C	D

1. Suppose you are studying the water from a pond and want to see if there are tiny things living in the water. Which of the tools shown would be most useful?

    A. A   C. C

    B. B   D. D

2. You are on a field trip to a pond. You want to be able to show your class where you were. Which of the tools would be most useful?

    A. A   C. C

    B. B   D. D

3. Scientists try to solve problems and answer questions. Which of the following is not a scientific question that a scientist might try to answer?

    A. How many frogs are in a pond?

    B. How do birds learn their "songs"?

    C. Are skateboards more fun than bicycles?

    D. Are earthquakes and volcanoes caused by the same thing?

4. What is the best way to make sure a measurement is accurate?

    A. Measure several times.

    B. Have someone else measure things for you.

    C. Use at least two different instruments to measure.

    D. Compare how similar your guess and your measurement are.

5. What is a claim?

   A. a law of nature that everyone knows

   B. a clue that helps you solve a problem

   C. a statement that someone wants you to believe is true

   D. an animal with a two-piece shell that lives in the water

6. Imagine reading a news story about a scientist who claims that eating potato chips makes people smarter. What kinds of questions would you ask that scientist? What kinds of evidence would you want to see before you believe the scientist's claim?

   _____

   _____

   _____

   _____

   _____

PEOPLE IN SCIENCE

René-Antoine Ferchault de Réaumur
(France 1683–1757)

René-Antoine Ferchault de Réaumur was the most important *entomologist* (someone who studies insects) of his time. Europe was lucky that he did study insects. The continent experienced a paper shortage in the early eighteenth century; cloth rags that were used to make paper were scarce. On a walk through the woods, de Réaumur noticed a wasp nest and realized it was made of paper. His study of wasps' digestive systems then helped him understand how the insects use wood to create the paper for their nests. In 1719, he presented to the French Academy his method for making paper from wood, helping to end the paper shortage. But de Réaumur studied more than just insects. He created a new type of thermometer. He improved the way iron was made by building a special furnace. He investigated the make-up of Chinese porcelain and found a new way to make it. He was also a writer; his six-volume *Memoirs Serving as a Natural History of Insects* was considered a milestone in the study of insect life.

Activity 1

Greenhouse-in-a-Bag

Review 1 talked about the scientific method, which is the way scientists find answers to their questions. This activity will give you a chance to explore the scientific method.

Using What You Know

You probably know that seeds need certain things to germinate (sprout) and grow. If you want to experiment to find out how water affects the ability of seeds to germinate, here is a way to do that:

Step 1: Get the following materials from your teacher: 20 seeds of the same kind, two Ziploc bags, two paper towels, enough water to wet one of the paper towels, two pieces of masking tape (2 inches each), and a pen to write on the masking tape.

Step 2: Stick one piece of masking tape on each bag. On one piece of tape, write "WATER." On the second piece of tape, write "NO WATER."

Step 3: Fold each paper towel to a size that will fit in a Ziploc bag.

Step 4: Put a dry, folded paper towel in the "NO WATER" bag so that the bag and towel are flat.

Step 5: Wet the second folded towel with a little water so that it is wet but not dripping water. Put the towel in the "WATER" bag so that the bag and towel are flat.

Step 6: Put 10 seeds on top of the paper towel in each bag; spread the seeds around so that you can easily see them.

Step 7: Find a place where you can lay the bags so that you can observe them for four to five days. A countertop or windowsill will work.

Step 8: Answer the following questions. Then, on the lines provided, write down the date you started this experiment and make observations about your seeds every day.

What is the question you are trying to answer?

_____

_____

What variable are you checking to see how it affects seed germination?

_____

What do you predict will happen to the seeds in each bag?

_____

_____

After you have completed the experiment, use these lines to write down how the actual results match your prediction.

_____

_____

Starting date: _____

Day 1: _____

Day 2: _____

Day 3: _____

Day 4: _____

Day 5: _____

Think It Over

Jim has decided to plant three different kinds of sweet corn in his garden: Candy Corn, Sweet Kernel, and Early Ear. He wants to know which type of corn produces the most ears.

1. Help Jim plan his experiment. Write down three things that he will need to keep the same for each kind of corn.

   _____

   _____

   _____

2. Why should Jim keep as many things as possible the same?

   _____

   _____

   _____

3. What is the one thing that Jim should vary (change) in his experiment?

   _____

4. It is now the end of the summer, and Jim has picked his sweet corn. He has counted the number of ears he got from each kind of corn and written the information in the following table.

Type of Corn	Total Ears for 10 Plants
Candy Corn	20
Sweet Kernel	30
Early Ear	10

   Which kind of corn produced the most ears?

   _____

5. Pretend that Jim made a mistake and added twice as much fertilizer to the Sweet Kernel corn only. The other kinds of corn received the original amount of fertilizer. Why would this make Jim's experiment less helpful to him?

_____

_____

_____

_____

6. If a variable were changed, such as the amount of water or light the plants received, how would that affect your conclusions about what kind of corn produces the most ears?

_____

_____

_____

_____

Activity 2

Tip to Tip

In Review 2, you learned more about using special tools, or instruments, to make measurements. You also talked about being precise (as exact as possible) in your measurements. This activity will give you some practice at making measurements. You will also compare similar measurements made by different people.

Using What You Know

You will need a one-meter length of string and a meter stick.

Step 1: Ask a partner to use the string to measure the distance from the tip of your nose to the tip of your middle finger. To do this, stretch your arm straight out from your side so that it is parallel to the ground. Keep your head facing directly forward, as shown in the diagram. Hold the end of the string against the tip of your nose while your partner holds the other end against the fingertip of your outstretched arm. Your partner can pinch the other end of the string at the tip of your middle finger. Be sure your partner keeps that place on the string marked.

Next, your partner should measure that length of string with a meter stick. Write your partner's name and the measurement she or he made in the table provided after Step 2.

Step 2: Ask four classmates to repeat the measurement of the distance from the tip of your nose to the tip of your finger. Record those measurements in the following table.

My Nose-to-Fingertip Length

Name of Person Measuring	Measurement to the Nearest Centimeter
Average Measurement	

Step 3: Determine the average measurement from the tip of your nose to the tip of your finger. To do this, add the measurements in your table. Then divide by the number of measurements you recorded. Write this number in the correct place in the table.

Think It Over

1. Were all the measurements of your nose-to-fingertip length the same?

_____

2. What are some things that could have affected the measurements?

_____

_____

_____

3. What is the reason for collecting five measurements?

_____

_____

4. Imagine that your teacher asks you to compare the nose-to-fingertip length of all the students in your class. What data will be most important to record for each person?

_____

_____

_____

5. Describe how you would make a bar graph to show the nose-to-fingertip data for your class. What kind of information should you include?

_____

_____

_____

Find out the average nose-to-fingertip length for five classmates. Then use the space below to create a bar graph that shows this information.

Activity 3

Mysterious Signs

Imagine that you are in the northern United States in winter. You and a friend decide to go out walking in the woods after a snowfall. The sun is bright as it reflects off of the fresh snow, and the woods are very quiet. The loudest sound you hear is your boots crunching in the snow. Suddenly, you and your friend notice some animal tracks and a few feathers up ahead in the snow. You wonder what happened at this place.

Using What You Know

Your job is to look at the evidence that can be found in the woods and the snow. Then you will evaluate the evidence and decide on a good explanation.

Step 1: Make up two explanations for what could have happened.

Explanation 1: _____

_____

_____

Explanation 2: _____

_____

_____

Step 2: List the evidence you could use to support each explanation.

Evidence for Explanation 1: _____

_____

_____

_____

Evidence for Explanation 2: _____

_____

_____

_____

Think It Over

1. How is the evidence that supports Explanation 1 like the evidence that
   supports Explanation 2?

_____

_____

_____

_____

2. How is the evidence that supports Explanation 1 different from the
   evidence that supports Explanation 2?

_____

_____

_____

_____

3. Right now, you don't have enough data to decide for sure what happened. What other data could help you decide which of the two explanations is more likely to be true?

_____

_____

_____

_____

4. Suppose that the tracks in the snow were different from what is pictured at the beginning of this activity. Instead, imagine that there were only bird tracks in the snow. There was one set of bird tracks leading to the place where the feathers were but no tracks at all leading away from it. How would your explanations change?

_____

_____

_____

_____

UNIT 2

Physical Science

Review 5

Properties of Matter

Scientists are always looking for clues to help them better understand nature. They have found that all of the objects in the world have one thing in common: Every substance that takes up space is made of **matter**. The smallest pieces of matter are **atoms**; atoms can connect together to create **molecules**. Scientists spend a lot of time studying different kinds of matter. This review is about matter and how it can change.

What Do You Think?

Have you ever cooked something? When food is cooked, it usually cannot be *un*-cooked. When food is frozen, however, it can go back to its original form by being thawed. Knowing whether or not the foods can go back to their original state will help you decide if a **physical change** or a **chemical change** has happened.

1. What happens to an egg when you cook it? In the space below, draw how a cooked egg is different from a raw egg.

Key Words

atom

chemical change

chemical property

gas

liquid

matter

molecule

physical change

physical property

solid

state of matter

volume

2. Describe the changes that take place in the egg when it is cooked.

_____

_____

3. Do you think that making ice cubes from liquid water is a physical or a chemical change?

_____

What People Think

When scientists study matter, they study *properties*. Properties include such things as whether a kind of matter sinks or floats, whether electricity can flow through it, whether it is magnetic, and how it behaves around other kinds of matter. Some of these properties are **physical properties**, and some are **chemical properties**. A physical property is something that you can observe about matter without changing the kind of matter it is.

4. List at least three physical properties of a piece of paper.

_____

_____

_____

On the other hand, scientists can study chemical properties of matter only by changing it into a different kind of matter.

5. Which of the following is a chemical property of a piece of typing paper?
    A. It is 8 inches wide and 11.5 inches long.
    B. It can be wadded up into a ball.
    C. It burns at 451°F.
    D. It is flat.

Just as matter can have physical and chemical properties, it can also change in two different ways. In a physical change, something becomes different in size, shape, appearance, or **state of matter**. A physical change can be undone, and it doesn't change the kind of matter that a thing is made of. A chemical change, however, turns one kind of matter into a different kind. A chemical change can't be undone.

Every kind of matter can exist in three states: **gas**, **liquid**, and **solid**. In the gas state, matter doesn't have a definite shape or **volume** (the amount of space it takes up). In the liquid state, matter has a definite volume, but not a definite shape. Solids have both a definite shape and volume.

Let's go back to our water example from Number 3. Water can be solid ice, liquid water for drinking, or water vapor (gas) in the air. You can see now that freezing or melting water is a physical change.

There's another important thing to keep in mind. When you change a substance's state of matter, the change can be reversed. For example, water (a liquid) can change to ice (a solid) and then back into water. It also can change to steam (a gas) and back into water again.

6. Explain how an aluminum soda can goes through different states of matter as it is made, used, recycled, and reused.

_____

_____

_____

Sometimes heating or cooling a material doesn't change just its state of matter. In this case, the heat causes the material to change into a different kind of matter; this is a chemical change. For example, heat causes a chemical change when you cook an egg. Other times, simply mixing together two or more different kinds of matter can cause a chemical change. Have you ever seen an antacid tablet dissolve in water? The molecules of the tablet break down and give off bubbles, a gas, when it dissolves. This gas is a different kind of matter from the material in the tablet. A new kind of matter is created, so it is a chemical change.

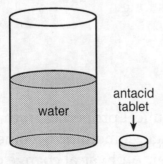
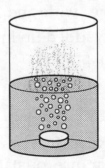

Practice Questions

. . . .

1. Review the differences between physical and chemical changes, then mark whether the following changes are physical or chemical.

   Roasting a marshmallow: _____

   Stirring salt into water: _____

   Making a snowball: _____

   Digesting food: _____

2. Imagine that you have two potatoes. One potato has rotted. You have mashed the other potato. You want to decide which of the two potatoes has gone through a chemical change. What information will help you decide?

   A. Both potatoes have brown skin.

   B. The shape of the mashed potato has changed.

   C. The mashed potato has become softer than it was.

   D. The smell and the color of the rotting potato have changed.

3. Which of the following actions causes only a physical change and not a chemical change?

   A. tearing tissue paper

   B. burning a match

   C. using a battery

   D. baking a cake

4. When air is let out of a tire, what physical change(s) does the air go through?

   A. It changes state.

   B. It changes shape.

   C. It changes volume.

   D. It changes shape and volume.

5. What could you do to show that water changing to ice is a physical change?

_____

_____

_____

_____

PEOPLE IN SCIENCE

William Perkin
(England 1838–1907)

When he was 19, William Perkin was a chemistry research assistant in London. His job was to find a use for coal tar—a black, gooey material left over when coal is made into fuel. One thing found in coal tar is aniline. Aniline is similar to quinine, the medicine used to cure malaria. Because there was a shortage of quinine in England, Perkin decided to try changing the aniline in coal tar into quinine. He tried some different mixtures. To his surprise, one mixture turned mauve, a shade of purple. He had invented a new kind of dye. Perkin's father used his life savings to set up a small dye factory. Soon, the new color was everywhere. Even Queen Victoria wore clothes colored with Perkin's dye. Although Perkin never made quinine from coal tar, his dye made him wealthy enough to retire when he was 36 years old.

Review 6

Energy

We talk about energy all the time. If you get tired, you might say that you *ran out* of energy. If you're playing with kittens who seem to be running all over the place, you might say that the kittens have *too much* energy. But exactly what is energy? In science, **energy** is the ability to make something move or change. This review will take a look at how energy works and some of the forms it takes.

What Do You Think?

When you see something advertised as being "free," it's wise to be careful. You should look carefully at what is being offered. Is there really no cost?

1. Have you ever heard the saying "There's no such thing as a free lunch"? What do you think this means?

   _____

   _____

2. Any time you want to lift or move something, you need to use energy. Where do you get this energy?

   _____

   _____

What People Think

We talk about energy all the time. There are lots of different kinds of energy. One kind is **chemical energy**. In Review 5, you learned that everything is made of tiny particles of matter called *atoms*. You also learned that atoms can join together to form molecules. Chemical energy is the energy stored in the connections between the atoms of molecules. This energy can be released when the connections are broken.

Key Words

chemical energy

circuit

conservation of energy

electrical energy

energy

mechanical energy

transform

Many other kinds of energy exist, too. There is heat energy and light energy. **Mechanical energy** is energy of motion and of the position of things. **Electrical energy** causes charged particles to move through wires. All of these forms of energy can be **transformed**, or changed, from one form to another.

3. Which of these is an example of heat and light energy?
    A. sunshine
    B. CD music
    C. hot chocolate
    D. boiling water

Any time energy is transformed, the total amount of energy that exists stays the same. In science, we say that energy is *conserved*. When the word *conserved* is used this way, a scientist doesn't mean that the lights were turned off when people left the room (although that's a good thing to do!). Instead, the scientist means that it is possible to know where all energy comes from and where it goes. In other words, energy doesn't appear or disappear, it only changes form. Let's look at an example to see what **conservation of energy** is all about.

Suppose you are heating water over a candle. Burning the candle transforms the candle's chemical energy into heat and light energy. The heat energy is then added to the water. Adding heat energy to the water makes the water molecules move around faster and faster, so the temperature goes up. It's very important to remember, though, that the water can get only as much energy as the candle gives off and no more. We can't get more energy from something than that thing already has. Energy is never created or destroyed. It only changes form.

4. Review for a minute what chemical and physical changes are. Is heating water a chemical or physical change?

_____

As you can see from the candle example, some chemical changes give off energy. Chemical changes that give off energy also happen any time you eat food. When you eat, you take in the chemical energy stored in the food. Your body can then use this energy to pump your heart, make new cells, walk, and do all of the things your body needs to do. If your body doesn't use the energy right away, it stores the extra energy as fat.

5. In order for you to walk, your body has to change the chemical energy of food into what other kind of energy?

_____

When your body temperature goes up, the chemical energy of food has been transformed into what other kind of energy?

_____

It is easy to see that the chemical energy from food you've eaten is being changed to mechanical energy, the energy of motion. But any time energy is transformed, some heat is given off. For example, rubbing your hands together makes them heat up. You know that energy is conserved (none is created or destroyed), so you can do a simple math problem. The mechanical energy (motion) *plus* the heat energy you feel is *equal to* the amount of chemical energy you've used. Some amount of heat energy is always given off when energy changes from one form to another.

Here's another example of energy being transformed: Batteries have chemicals inside them. When batteries are connected to wires in a closed loop, called a **circuit**, chemical changes happen inside the battery. These chemical changes make tiny particles move through the wires; this is electrical energy. Electrical energy can make a lightbulb shine or a radio play. Study the diagram shown here, then answer Number 6.

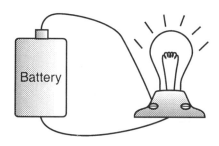

6. Which of the following is not a form of energy that exists in the circuit shown in the diagram?
    A. heat energy
    B. light energy
    C. chemical energy
    D. mechanical energy

Energy is always being transformed around us. Let's take one last look at some of those transformations.

7. Study the picture shown here.

List all the energy transformations happening in the picture that you can find.

_____

_____

_____

_____

Practice Questions

1. In which of these examples is energy changing from chemical to electrical energy?

    A. mixing together baking soda and vinegar

    B. moving heavy objects with a forklift

    C. a firefly shining its light at night

    D. using a battery-operated radio

2. When two certain chemicals are mixed together, they create a bright light. What kind of energy transformation is this?

    A. heat energy to light energy

    B. light energy to chemical energy

    C. chemical energy to light energy

    D. chemical energy to electrical energy

3. Suppose that you eat a candy bar shortly before running a race. Will your body transform all of the chemical energy from the candy bar into the mechanical energy of running?

    _____

    Explain why you think this.

    _____

    _____

    _____

    _____

4. A child gets a push while sitting on a swing. She then swings forward 5 feet above the ground. How high will she swing on the way back (on the return swing)?

    A. exactly 5 feet

    B. much less than 5 feet

    C. just a little less than 5 feet

    D. just a little higher than 5 feet

5. Imagine that a light shines on a solar calculator, and you use the calculator to add numbers. What kind of energy transformation is happening?

   A. light energy to heat energy

   B. light energy to electrical energy

   C. light energy to chemical energy

   D. light energy to mechanical energy

6. It can be said that when you eat an apple, you are eating energy from the sun. Explain how this can be so.

   _____

   _____

   _____

   _____

7. Which of the following is given off in all energy changes?

   A. heat energy   C. electrical energy

   B. light energy   D. mechanical energy

PEOPLE IN SCIENCE

Marie-Anne Lavoisier
(France 1758–1836)

When she was almost 14, Marie-Anne Paulze married chemist Antoine-Laurent Lavoisier and became his assistant. After learning Latin and English, she translated scientific texts for him. She helped with experiments, kept records of laboratory work, and wrote letters to other chemists. In 1789, she illustrated a chemistry book written by her husband. That book is considered to be the first modern chemistry textbook. Later, in 1805, an eight-volume set of books about chemistry was published. The author was listed as Antoine-Laurent Lavoisier. Actually, however, he had been put to death 11 years earlier, during the French Revolution. Instead, it was Marie who had written much of the material and had been responsible for getting the book published. Marie put Antoine's name on her books because she knew that, in those days, a woman in science would not be taken seriously.

Review 7

Motion

Have you ever seen a magician make something move with just a wave of a magic wand? Well, there is always some trick behind that magic movement because it is impossible for something to move without a push or a pull. This review will look at some basic rules for how things move.

What Do You Think?

Every day, you come across hundreds of examples of things being pushed or pulled. Think about it. What kind of pushing and pulling did you have to do just to get to this class today?

1. In the table shown here, list examples of pushing or pulling that you have done or seen. One of each is filled in for you.

Pushing Motions	Pulling Motions
a bulldozer pushing dirt	a tow truck pulling a car

Key Words

force

friction

gravity

What People Think

Think about riding a bicycle. If you are on a flat surface, you have to start pedaling or pushing with your foot to make the bike start moving. In other words, you create a **force**. There are forces in nature as well. When you are on a hill, you can just get on the bike and start moving downhill, even if you don't pedal or push. This is because **gravity** makes you move. No one knows exactly what gravity is. We just know that things attract, or pull, each other. The name for this pull is *gravity*. In the case of your bike on a hill, the earth's strong gravity is pulling you and your bike to a lower place on the earth.

2. What is another force that can attract, or pull, something without touching it?

    _____

3. What other things in nature provide forces that can make things move?

    _____

    _____

Ancient scientists knew that it takes a force to make something start to move. For a long time, however, they didn't know that *it also takes a force to make something stop moving or change direction.* The name for this force is **friction**. Friction is a force that causes two things to slow down when they rub against each other. Friction also causes things to heat up. Another word we often use for friction is *traction*. People who play basketball wear rubber-soled shoes because the rubber gives their feet good traction on a wood floor or concrete playground. You don't want your feet to slip when playing basketball!

4. Which of the following is used to lessen the force of friction?
    A. sand spread on ice or snow
    B. brakes on a car
    C. oil or grease
    D. rubber

All of this information about what makes things move and stop moving can be summed up in the following rule: *Things move only when a force moves them, and things keep moving until a force stops them.*

Now think again about riding a bike on a flat surface.

5. If you want to move your bike only 12 inches forward, how hard should you push or pedal it?

    _____

    If you want to move your bike the distance of one block as fast as possible, how hard should you push or pedal it?

    _____

Here's another question:

6. Imagine that you have a child carrier on your bike and want to give your two-year-old brother a ride somewhere. Will you have to pedal harder? Why or why not?

    _____

    _____

    _____

    _____

This takes us to another rule about motion: *The more force you use to push something, the faster it changes speed; and the more mass something has, the more force it takes to change its speed.* These rules can help you predict the motion of many different objects.

Practice Questions

1. Why is it easier to in-line skate downhill than uphill?

   _____

   _____

   _____

Directions: Use the following picture to answer Numbers 2 through 4.

2. In the picture, what is being moved by the force of gravity?
   A. the rope in tug-of-war
   B. the sailboat on the water
   C. the skier behind the boat
   D. the children on the water slide

3. In the game tug-of-war, two groups pull on the ends of a rope and try to make the other team cross a puddle or other mark. What decides which team will win a tug-of-war?

    A. the team with the longer piece of rope

    B. the team with the strongest people

    C. the team with the shortest people

    D. the team with the tallest people

4. In which activity is it better to have more friction than less friction?

    A. tug-of-war

    B. water skiing

    C. water sliding

    D. in-line skating

5. If you are swinging on the swings at the playground, what happens if you stop pumping your legs?

    A. You stop swinging immediately.

    B. It depends on how long the swing's chains are.

    C. The force of friction makes you slow down and stop.

    D. You keep swinging until you drag your feet on the ground.

6. If you pushed all of the following with the same force on a flat surface, which would roll fastest?

    A. a one-pound ball

    B. a two-pound ball

    C. a three-pound ball

    D. a four-pound ball

Review 8

Machines

If you were asked to mow the lawn or cut a piece of paper, you would most likely use some kind of **machine**. There are machines all around us. In the kitchen, we use machines to open cans, cook food, and keep things cold. Around the house, machines such as vacuum cleaners help us do our work. Machines are part of our everyday lives. This review looks at how machines help us all.

What Do You Think?

Sometimes it's easy to decide whether something is a machine or not. Of course, a car is a machine. It's big and powerful. But what would you say about a screwdriver? Is a screwdriver a machine? You may be surprised at some of the things that can be called machines.

1. Examine each object in the pictures shown here. On your own, circle which ones you think are machines. When you have finished, compare your selections with those of several classmates.

scissors   shovel   pencil sharpener   crane

lawn mower   hammer   blender   windmill

Key Words

fulcrum

lever

machine

work

What People Think

Machines are all about **work**. Work is done any time something is moved by pushing, pulling, lifting, turning, or stopping it. A machine is anything that helps us do work with less force or with greater speed. For example, a shovel is a machine because it helps you move material like dirt or snow faster than you could do it with your hands. The bigger the shovel, the more dirt or snow you can move at a time. A pair of scissors is also a simple machine. A pair of scissors helps cut things faster than a knife because a pair of scissors is really like two knives working together.

2. A hammer is a simple machine. How does it help you?

_____

_____

_____

A canoe paddle, a wheelbarrow, and a board on a **fulcrum** (the point the board rests on, like what holds a seesaw up) are all simple machines that use **levers**. Wheels, axles, and ramps also are examples of simple machines. While there are many different kinds of machines, they all have one main thing in common: All machines need force in order to work. They need some kind of push or pull. Sometimes, an engine provides the force. Other times, nature or people provide the force. The important thing is that machines need force to make them work.

3. What provides the force that makes a windmill go around?
   A. a pull
   B. nature
   C. a person
   D. an engine

Another important thing to remember about machines is that you don't get something for nothing. Think, for example, about a ramp. Imagine that you need to move a very heavy box to a shelf that is two feet above the floor. To lift it straight up with your arms would be very difficult. It would be much easier, however, if you could push it up a ramp to the shelf. Using the ramp would mean that you could use less force, but you would have to move the box a longer distance. If you use less force but go a longer distance, you still do the same amount of work. You don't get something for nothing, but a machine makes it easier to do the work.

Now that you've learned more about machines, let's go back to the first question in the review.

4. Is a screwdriver a machine?

_____

Why or why not?

_____

_____

_____

Practice Questions
· · · · · · · · · · · · · · · ·

Directions: Use the picture of a wheelbarrow shown here to answer Number 1.

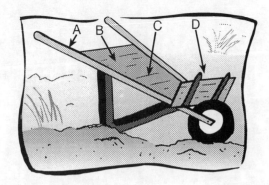

1. Where should you place a load in a wheelbarrow to make it easiest to lift?
   A. position A   C. position C
   B. position B   D. position D

2. A bicycle is a machine. Which part of the bicycle receives the force from the rider that makes it move forward?

    A. pedals

    B. rear wheel

    C. front wheel

    D. gear shifter

Directions: Use the picture shown here to answer Numbers 3 and 4.

3. In this picture, the ramp onto the truck is a simple machine. How does the ramp help the person at the back of the truck?

    A. The person at the back can get more exercise by using more force.

    B. The person at the back can move the boxes onto the truck with less force.

    C. The person at the back can move the boxes a shorter distance to the truck.

    D. The person at the back can move the boxes onto the truck faster because of stronger gravity.

4. If one person carries a box up the ramp to the truck and a second person lifts the same box directly on to the truck, which person does more work?

    A. The person lifting the box directly on to the truck does more work.

    B. The person carrying the box up the ramp does more work.

    C. They both do the same amount of work.

    D. There is no way to tell.

Review 9

Earth in Motion

As you sit reading this page, Earth is spinning around at about 800 kilometers per hour (500 miles per hour) and moving through space at 80,000 kilometers per hour (50,000 miles per hour). Can you feel it moving at these great speeds? What clues do you have that Earth is moving at all?

What Do You Think?

You are familiar with calendars; they help us keep track of days, weeks, months, and years. But do you know why calendars are made the way they are?

1. Why are Earth years 365 days long?

　　_____

　　_____

2. Why is there an extra day every "leap year"？

Key Words
axis
orbit
phase
revolution
rotation

　　_____

　　_____

　　_____

3. Why is a day on Earth equal to 24 hours?

_____

_____

What People Think

Many people have a hard time thinking about the large distances between objects in space. When we measure a distance on Earth, we might use miles or kilometers, feet or meters. In space, distances are often measured in *millions* of kilometers. That's one million times larger than the units you are used to. Think of how long it takes to walk or drive a kilometer. Now multiply that time and distance by one million! It's almost too huge to think about.

4. Using what you know about distances in space, which of the following is the average distance from the earth to the moon?
    A. about 239 feet
    B. about 239,000 miles
    C. about 384,000 meters
    D. about 384 kilometers

The imaginary line through the middle of the earth from the North Pole to the South Pole is the earth's **axis**. Earth spins on this axis, and the spinning is called **rotation**. Earth days are 24 hours long because that is about how long it takes for the earth to make one rotation.

Earth moves another way, too. **Revolution** is the movement of the earth as it moves around the sun. The path that the earth follows around the sun is its **orbit**. Earth's orbit is not exactly a circle; rather, its shape is like a circle that has been squished.

5. It takes the earth one _____ to revolve once around the sun.

As you probably know, there are nine planets in our solar system: Mercury, Venus, Earth, Mars, Jupiter, Saturn, Uranus, Neptune, and Pluto. All the planets rotate and revolve around the sun, just as Earth does. Each planet takes a different amount of time to do this, however. For example, on the planet Mercury, one rotation takes 59 Earth days; one revolution takes 88 Earth days.

6. If you were 10 Mercury years old, about how old would you be in Earth years?

Seven of the planets also have moons that rotate and revolve around them. Some planets have more than one moon; Saturn has at least 18 moons! You know that the way the earth's moon looks in the sky changes a little bit each day. Sometimes we can't see it at all, sometimes it looks like a tiny sliver, and sometimes it's full and round. These different shapes that we see are called **phases**. The four pictures that follow show four phases of the earth's moon.

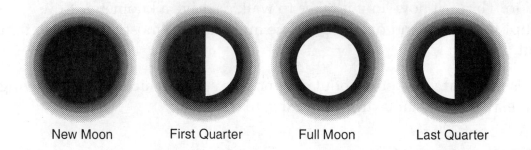

| New Moon | First Quarter | Full Moon | Last Quarter |

You will get a chance to learn more about the moon's phases in Activity 7.

Days and years aren't the only things caused by the way the earth moves; seasons are caused by the earth's movement, too. The earth's axis isn't straight up and down. Instead, it is tilted a little bit. The tilt stays about the same during the earth's entire orbit. This means that, when the earth is on one side of the sun, the Northern Hemisphere (the half of the earth where we live) is tilted toward the sun, and it is summer. When it is on the other side of the sun, the Northern Hemisphere is tilted away from the sun, and we have winter. The following diagrams can help you see how this works.

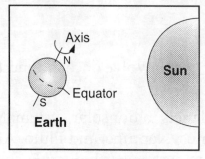

Summer in the Northern Hemisphere

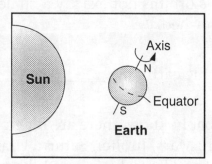

Winter in the Northern Hemisphere

Practice Questions

1. Which of the following is most like a basketball spinning on someone's fingertip?

    A. the earth rotating on its axis

    B. the planets orbiting the sun

    C. the earth revolving around the sun

    D. the moon traveling around the earth

2. Even with a powerful telescope, it is not always possible to see all the planets on any given night. Why is this?

    A. The sun is just too bright.

    B. The moon is just too bright.

    C. A planet may be hidden by a star.

    D. A planet may be hidden because it is on the other side of the earth.

3. Why haven't we traveled to many other planets in our solar system?

    _____

    _____

    _____

    _____

4. Which of the following statements is correct?

    A. The moon revolves around the sun while the sun revolves around the earth.

    B. The moon revolves around the earth while the earth revolves around the sun.

    C. The sun revolves around the earth while the moon revolves around the earth.

    D. The earth revolves around the moon while the moon revolves around the sun.

5. Each day, people on Earth experience a period of daytime and a period of nighttime. The reason that we have day and night is that
   A. the distance between the earth and the sun changes.
   B. the earth revolves around the sun.
   C. the earth rotates on its axis.
   D. the earth tilts on its axis.

6. The sun is at the center of our solar system. Which of the following is another word for our sun?
   A. star
   B. planet
   C. galaxy
   D. meteorite

PEOPLE IN SCIENCE

Archimedes

(Greece, around 287 B.C.–212 B.C.)

One of the greatest inventors and thinkers of ancient times was the Greek mathematician Archimedes. He showed how levers could lift great weights, and he invented the compound pulley, with which he is said to have lifted a ship full of passengers. He is credited with inventing an irrigation system. He was a master of thinking up tools of war, including a catapult to hurl rocks and burning objects. He also solved problems for the king of his region. The king once suspected his goldsmith of cheating him by including other, lesser metals in a supposedly gold crown. He asked Archimedes to prove the trickery.

Archimedes was having trouble with the problem, until one day he climbed out of the bathtub and noticed how the water level dropped. The tub was more full with him in it than after he climbed out. He made the connection between his body volume and the weight of water he displaced. As the story goes, the idea so excited him that he ran out onto the streets without bothering to dress, shouting "Eureka!" (I have found it!). He tested the crown using this idea of displacement and discovered the king had indeed been cheated. He also used this same idea to explain how objects float in liquid.

Review 10

Earth's Weather

The earth is surrounded by layers of air called the **atmosphere**. The atmosphere is important to us for many reasons. It holds the oxygen we need to breathe, and it gives us some protection from the sun's rays. Every day, you can also see that the atmosphere is changing. These daily changes are the **weather**. The sun, the atmosphere, and the things that happen on the surface of the earth all cause changes in the weather. In this review, you'll take a look at some of the things that affect our weather.

Key Words

air pressure

atmosphere

condensation

evaporation

forecast

high pressure area

humidity

low pressure area

meteorologist

precipitation

water cycle

water vapor

weather

What Do You Think?

If you've ever been caught outside during a rain shower, you know that clouds store water. But have you ever wondered where the water in the clouds comes from?

1. The way that water gets into the clouds and then falls back to the ground is called the **water cycle**. In the following box, draw and label a diagram showing how you think water gets into the clouds and turns into **precipitation** (water in some form that falls to the ground).

2. What determines whether the precipitation falls as rain or snow?

_____

_____

What People Think

If you set a cold glass of water in the hot sun, you know that drops of water will form on the outside of the glass. This isn't because the glass has holes that allow water to leak through! These drops are **condensation**. The cold temperature of the glass has caused **water vapor** (gas) in the air to condense, or form into drops of liquid water, on the outside of the glass.

You probably also know that if you leave a glass of water sitting out for some time, the water in the glass will disappear. Where does it go? The process of **evaporation** causes the liquid water from the glass to turn into water vapor and rise into the air. Meteorologists measure **humidity**, which is the amount of water vapor in the air.

3. Now look back at the diagram of the water cycle that you drew in "What Do You Think?" and see if you need to make any changes using this information. Use the terms *condensation*, *water vapor*, and *evaporation* to label your diagram.

The water cycle is a very important part of weather on Earth. The energy that makes the water cycle happen comes from the sun. The sun warms the land and the water on the earth so that the water evaporates and forms clouds. After the water from the clouds falls back to the earth as precipitation, the cycle starts over again.

4. Many people pay a lot of attention to predictions about precipitation. List at least three reasons that it can be important to know what kind of precipitation will fall and how much.

_____

_____

_____

Precipitation is only one thing that weather scientists, called **meteorologists**, study. They study many other features of the weather, too.

  5. Which of the following is not a feature of the weather?
     A. the kind of clouds
     B. the speed of the wind
     C. the position of the stars
     D. the temperature of the air

All over the world, people are collecting data about the weather. This information is fed into computers and recorded on maps and charts. Then meteorologists study what is happening and use their knowledge to **forecast** the weather to come.

Forecasting the weather is very difficult because there are so many things that can affect the weather and change it. There are a few "rules of thumb" to follow, however. For example, meteorologists know the following:

- Weather systems on the United States mainland generally move from west to east.

- The air in Earth's atmosphere goes up for miles. The weight of all this air is called **air pressure**. Winds in **high pressure areas** rotate clockwise, and winds in **low pressure areas** rotate in the opposite direction, counterclockwise.

- High pressure areas usually have clear skies, and low pressure areas usually have clouds.

- When warm, moist air collides with (bumps into) cool, dry air, we can usually count on having precipitation—maybe even a thunderstorm.

Meteorologists have many instruments to collect the data they use to make weather forecasts. The instrument you are probably most familiar with is the thermometer.

6. List some other instruments that help meteorologists collect data about the weather and conditions in the atmosphere. Then tell what each instrument measures.

Instrument: _____

Measures: _____

Instrument: _____

Measures: _____

Instrument: _____

Measures: _____

Practice Questions

1. In some very hot places on Earth, clouds produce rain, but the rain does not reach the ground. This is because the rain
   A. falls to the ground as a thick fog.
   B. is blown by wind to other places.
   C. condenses into thunder and lightning.
   D. evaporates before reaching the ground.

2. Imagine that it has been hot and humid for the past few days. Today, the barometric pressure (air pressure) is falling quickly. These observations most likely mean that
   A. a warm front is coming into the area.
   B. there will be a thunderstorm.
   C. temperatures will rise.
   D. a cold front is leaving.

Directions: The map here shows one high pressure area in the United States on Tuesday evening. Use this information to answer Number 3.

3. Which of the following maps shows the most likely location of the high pressure area on Wednesday?

A.

C.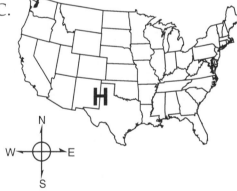

B.

D.

Directions: Use the following information to answer Number 4. The weather symbols in the box are used to show wind strength on a weather map.

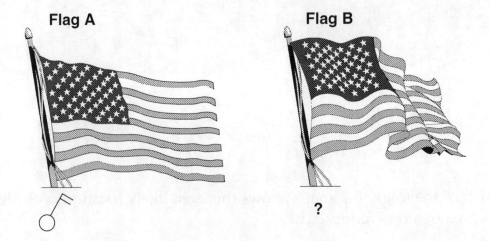

stronger wind ⟶

Flags A and B are in two different cities. The wind symbol for the city of Flag A is shown below the flagpole.

Flag A   **Flag B**

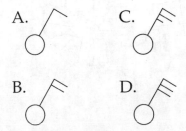

?

4. What wind symbol would be used for the city where Flag B is located?

    A.   C.

    B.   D.

5. Your town is in a high pressure area. This means that
    A. it is probably snowing.
    B. it is probably raining.
    C. it is probably sunny.
    D. it is probably cold.

Review 11

The Rock Cycle

In the last review, you learned more about the weather, which is always changing. Another thing that is always changing is the surface of the earth. The weather can change in minutes, but changes to the earth's surface often take much longer—months, years, even millions of years. This review will discuss the **rock cycle**, which is just one part of the changes always happening on the surface of the earth.

What Do You Think?

The following illustration shows a rock. You can see that it is not all one color.

1. What causes the rock to have several colors?

   _____

   _____

   _____

2. What would happen if you hit this rock several times with a hammer? What would the rock look like?

   _____

   _____

   _____

Key Words

erosion

igneous rock

lava

magma

metamorphic rock

mineral

rock cycle

sedimentary rock

weathering

What People Think

Have you ever thought about what rocks are made of? If you look closely at a rock, you can see that it is made of many smaller pieces. These pieces are called **minerals**. These minerals are different shapes, sizes, and colors, which helps us to tell them apart. They can also be identified by how much they sparkle or by how hard they are. Even if a large rock is broken into small pieces, the smaller pieces contain the same minerals that make up the larger rock. Sometimes the minerals in a rock are very large and easy to see. Other times, they are very small and can be seen only with a magnifying lens. In some rocks, the minerals are so small that special microscopes must be used to see them.

3. If a rock is all one color, does it mean that the rock is made of only one mineral? Why do you think this?

_____

_____

_____

Nearly everything in nature exists in cycles, or repeating patterns. Rocks move through a cycle that may take millions of years. At the core of the earth, the rock is so hot that it becomes liquid. The liquid rock is called **magma**. When the liquid rock rises to the surface of the earth, such as when a volcano erupts, it is called **lava**. Magma and lava cool to form **igneous rock**. Granite is an example of igneous rock.

If igneous or sedimentary rock is buried under a mountain, or deep in the earth's crust, it changes to **metamorphic rock**. Shale is one example of metamorphic rock.

Small pieces of rocks are always being broken off and worn away; this is called **weathering**. Wind and rain can wash these small pieces away so that they collect somewhere else; this is **erosion**. The tiny pieces can build up and form layers over the ground where they collect, and sometimes these layers are pressed together enough to make **sedimentary rock**. Limestone and sandstone are two common types of sedimentary rock.

4. In which of the following types of rock would fossils most likely be found?

   A. magma rock   C. sedimentary rock

   B. igneous rock   D. metamorphic rock

   Why do you think this?

   _____

   _____

5. A strong hit from a hammer can help to break apart a rock. Natural processes also help to weather rocks. Which of the following is not a natural process that wears down rocks into small pieces?

   A. waves

   B. glaciers

   C. changes in the air pressure

   D. water freezing and melting in the cracks of a rock

Rock is not the only thing that can be eroded. Have you ever been in a sandbox or on a sandy beach on a windy day? If so, you've probably felt sand being blown away by the wind.

6. Name at least two other examples of erosion.

   _____

   _____

Practice Questions
. . . .

1. How can you tell that a rock has been weathered for a long time?

   A. It is jagged and rough.

   B. It is rounded and smooth.

   C. It is softer than other rocks.

   D. It is harder than other rocks.

Directions: The following picture shows a mountain as it looks today. Use this information to answer Number 2.

2. Which of these pictures most likely shows the same mountain the furthest into the future?

A.    C.

B.    D.

Why do you think so?

_____

_____

_____

_____

3. What is one way to keep soil from eroding?
    A. Keep water running over it.
    B. Build walking trails over it.
    C. Plant trees or crops in it.
    D. Build houses on it.

4. Which of the following statements is false?

   A. Sedimentary rock can be made from magma.

   B. Sedimentary rock can be made from igneous rock.

   C. Sedimentary rock can be made from metamorphic rock.

   D. Sedimentary rock can be made from other sedimentary rock.

5. On the picture of the rock cycle that follows, write in the missing rock types in the correct oval.

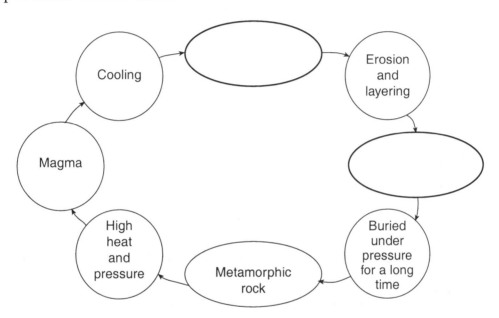

PEOPLE IN SCIENCE

William Smith was in charge of the construction of a canal. One day, he noticed something interesting. There were a lot of fossils in the ground where his men were digging, and the fossils were in layers. Each kind of fossil was found only in its own layer. Probably a lot of other people had seen this; no one, however, had ever thought about what it meant. Smith was the first person to pay

William Smith
(England 1769–1839)

attention to the regular and orderly way each fossil layer was formed. He discovered that he could tell how old a fossil was by which layer it was in. Because he enjoyed studying these fossils, Smith switched careers from construction to geology. He made a map of England showing where different rock layers could be found. His map is still used today.

Activity 4

Physical Changes

In Review 5, you learned about physical properties. Remember that physical properties are things that can be observed without changing the kind of matter something is made of. Some examples of physical properties are size, shape, color, odor, and state of matter (gas, liquid, or solid). Physical changes happen when one or more physical properties change, but the kind of matter stays the same. In a chemical change, on the other hand, the kind of matter does change.

Using What You Know

This activity is in two parts: "Shape" and "State of Matter."

Part 1: Shape

Your teacher will give you a balloon for this portion of the activity. Do not share your balloon with anyone.

Step 1: Place a balloon on your desk. Do not blow it up. In the box below, draw a picture of your balloon.

Step 2: Now blow up the balloon. Pinch the opening shut and hold it in front of you. Be sure you use the hand that you <u>do not</u> use for writing to do this. In the box below, draw a picture of your blown-up balloon.

What changed about the balloon?

_____

_____

Is it a physical or chemical change?

_____

Step 3: Keep holding onto the balloon as you slowly let the air out.

How does the shape of the balloon in Step 3 compare to the way it looked in Steps 1 and 2?

_____

_____

How does this help you decide whether it went through a physical or chemical change?

_____

_____

Part 2: State of Matter

In this portion of the activity, you will experiment with ways to change water vapor in the air to liquid water.

Step 4: Walk over to a window. Put your face as close to the window as you can without touching it. Blow softly onto the window.

What forms on the window?

_____

_____

_____

Where did it come from?

_____

_____

_____

Step 5: Blow up your balloon again. Hold the open end of the balloon very close to the windowpane. Hold onto the balloon while you let the air out onto the window.

What forms on the window?

_____

_____

_____

How does the result of Step 5 compare to what happened in Step 4?

_____

_____

_____

Think It Over

1. Did the balloon have more rubber when it was blown up in Step 2 than in Step 1? Why do you think so?

_____

_____

_____

_____

2. Why do you think the results of Steps 4 and 5 were so much alike?

_____

_____

_____

_____

3. What are some other examples of liquid water forming from water in the air?

_____

_____

_____

_____

Activity 5

The Sun's Energy

You use things that have been heated every day. Maybe you take a hot shower or bath; maybe you use a hair dryer on your hair; and maybe you eat a hot meal in the evening. Water, air, and food are just a few of the things we heat every day. You know that if something has been heated, energy has been transformed, or changed from one form to another. In this activity, you will use the sun's energy to heat tissue paper.

Using What You Know

It is best to do this activity at around noon on a sunny day. Your teacher will give you a magnifying lens and some tissue paper.

CAUTION: Do **not** look at the sun through the magnifying lens. Do **not** focus the sun's light on anything except as directed in this activity.

Step 1: Place the piece of tissue paper on a sidewalk away from other things.

Step 2: Hold the magnifying lens above the tissue paper so that it focuses a spot of light that is about the size of a quarter. Hold the lens in this position for about 10 seconds. At the end of this time, move the lens away from the paper. Use the table that follows Step 4 to write down what happened to the paper.

Step 3: Hold the magnifying lens above the tissue paper so that it focuses a spot of light that is about the size of a dime. Hold the lens in this position for about 10 seconds. At the end of this time, move the lens away from the paper. Use the table that follows Step 4 to write down what happened to the paper.

Step 4: Hold the magnifying lens above the tissue paper so that it focuses a spot of light that is about the size of the period at the end of this sentence. Hold the lens in this position for about 10 seconds. At the end of this time, move the lens away from the paper. Use the table to write down what happened to the paper.

Sunlight Spot	What Happened to the Tissue Paper
spot about the size of a quarter	
spot about the size of a dime	
spot about the size of a period	

Think It Over

1. What happened as the spot of sunlight through the magnifying lens got smaller and smaller?

_____

_____

_____

2. Describe the energy changes that happen when the sun shines on the tissue paper.

_____

_____

_____

3. When you eat a vegetable or a piece of fruit, you are eating energy from the sun. Explain how this can be.

_____

_____

_____

Activity 6

Balancing Act

You learned about some simple machines in Review 9. One kind of simple machine is a lever. A lever can be any kind of stiff board or bar resting on and moving around a support point. Remember that this support point is called a *fulcrum*. One kind of lever that you have probably used on the playground is a seesaw.

Using What You Know

You and a partner will make your own seesaw using a ruler. Your teacher will give you directions for how to make the seesaw lever. Be sure that the 0 cm mark is on the left and the 30 cm mark is on the right. After you have made your lever, practice balancing it by placing it on the fulcrum so that both ends of the ruler are in the air.

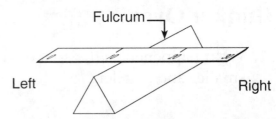

Balancing Act A

Use three of the pennies your teacher gave you for this portion of the activity.

Step 1: Place one penny on the ruler so that its center is at about the 29 cm line.

Step 2: Stack the other two pennies and place them on the opposite side of the fulcrum.

Step 3: Slide the stack of pennies along the ruler until it is balanced and both of its ends are in the air.

Step 4: Record the positions of the pennies by drawing them on the ruler that follows.

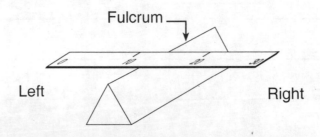

Balancing Act B

You will need one more penny for Balancing Act B.

Step 5: Don't move the stack of pennies from Step 3.

Step 6: Add a penny on top of the penny that is at 29 cm.

Step 7: Slide the new stack of pennies along the ruler until the ruler is balanced once again.

Step 8: Record the positions of the pennies by drawing them on the ruler that follows.

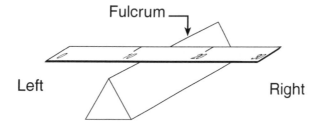

Balancing Act C

You will need one more penny for Balancing Act C.

Step 9: Put a third penny on top of the right-hand stack from Step 7.

Step 10: Slide the stack of three along the ruler until it balances.

Step 11: Record the positions of the pennies by drawing them on the ruler that follows.

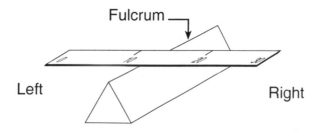

Balance Challenge 1

Step 1: Put a stack of two pennies anywhere on the ruler.

Step 2: Challenge your partner to predict where to place another two pennies to balance the ruler and pennies.

Step 3: Check your partner's prediction by trying it.

Balance Challenge 2

Step 4: Your partner should now challenge you with a different stack of pennies in a different position on the ruler.

Step 5: Continue to play this game until you and your partner are both pretty good at making predictions.

Think It Over

1. Write a rule to explain how to balance the seesaw lever when one side has a heavier weight than the other.

   _____

   _____

   _____

   _____

2. Look back at your drawing for Balancing Act A. Notice the positions of the pennies. Now imagine that you tip the ruler up and down like a seesaw. Which will move farther through the air each time the ruler is tipped, the stack of two pennies or the penny that is by itself?

   _____

Make a sketch to explain your answer:

3. Write a general rule for balancing the seesaw.

_____

_____

_____

_____

Activity 7

The Earth and the Moon

In this activity, you'll investigate how the earth and the moon move around the sun.

Using What You Know

Your teacher will give you a pin and three Styrofoam balls. The blue ball represents Earth, the yellow ball represents the sun, and the ball that is half black and half white represents the moon.

Step 1: Push the pin into the blue Earth ball to show where your town is located on the planet.

Step 2: Set the Earth ball and the sun ball on your desk or a table to show your town at night. Draw a diagram of this arrangement in the following box.

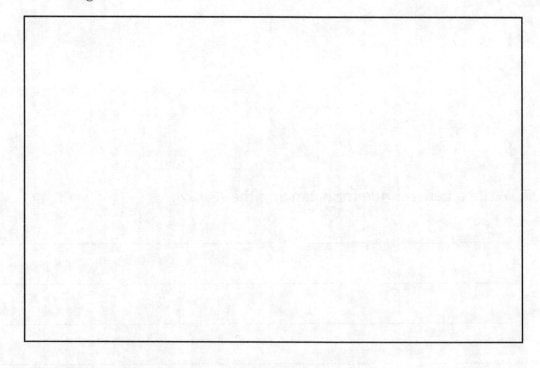

Step 3: Keep the sun and the earth in the arrangement from Step 2. Now move the moon ball counterclockwise in a circle once around the earth. This is one **revolution**. During this revolution, the black side of the ball must always be facing away from the sun. Practice this step three times.

Step 4: The earth revolves around the sun counterclockwise. Using the Styrofoam balls, move the earth in one revolution around the sun.

Step 5: At the same time that the earth revolves around the sun, it **rotates**, or spins, counterclockwise on its axis. The axis is the imaginary line that runs from the North Pole to the South Pole. Each rotation takes about one day. As the earth rotates, half of the planet is always facing the sun, and half is always facing away from the sun. Practice this rotation of the earth three times.

Think It Over

1. What does the black half of the moon ball represent?

_____

_____

_____

Why does the black half of the moon always face away from the sun?

_____

_____

_____

2. As the moon revolves around the earth, people on the earth see different amounts of light reflecting off of the moon. This is why we see different phases of the moon. Shown here are the pictures of four of the moon phases that you saw in Review 10. Also shown here is a diagram of the sun, the earth, and the moon in four different positions as it revolves around the earth. Study the diagrams, then match the position of the moon with the phase that people on the earth see.

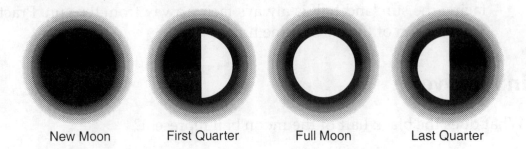

New Moon   First Quarter   Full Moon   Last Quarter

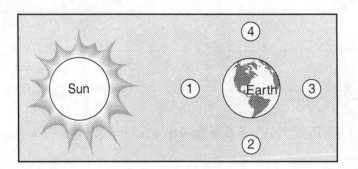

Position 1—Phase: _____

Position 2—Phase: _____

Position 3—Phase: _____

Position 4—Phase: _____

3. You know that as the earth rotates on its axis, it is also revolving around the sun. How many rotations of the earth occur during one revolution around the sun?

_____

UNIT 3

Life Science

Review 12

Living and Nonliving Things

How can you tell if something is **living** or **nonliving**? This may seem like a silly question, but it's not. Scientists put things into groups so they can study them. They group things by describing their characteristics, or features: whether they are living or nonliving, what they are made of, what they look like, where they are found, and so on. For example, people and pine trees are both living things, but they are very different. So, scientists put people and pine trees into different groups. Once you learn how to group living things, it is much easier to study them.

What Do You Think?

Let's start by thinking about some things that are familiar to you.

1. Think about two different things: one that is living and one that is nonliving. Write each one on the correct line provided. On the lines marked "Characteristics," list the characteristics each thing has that help you know it is living or nonliving.

   Living thing: _____

   Characteristics: _____

   _____

   Nonliving thing: _____

   Characteristics:_____

   _____

   _____

Key Words
amphibian

biologist

classify

insect

invertebrate

living

mammal

nonliving

organism

species

vertebrate

Compare your lists with other students' lists. Do they have any characteristics for their living or nonliving things that you do not have on your list? Are there any characteristics that you wrote down for one of the lists that someone else wrote down for the other list?

2. Is it a problem if a certain characteristic appears in both a "living thing" list and a "nonliving thing" list? Why do you think this?

_____

_____

_____

What People Think

When people organize things into groups, we say that they are **classifying** those things. People classify things according to their characteristics.

3. Which of the following should not be classified as something that people use for writing?

   A. a magic marker   C. a toothbrush

   B. a stick of chalk   D. a pen

If something is to be classified as living, it must do all of the following things:

- It must be made up of cells.

- It must need water and food.

- It must grow.

- It must be able to reproduce itself.

- It must be able to respond to changes in the place where it lives.

Almost every living thing—from the tiniest one-celled **organism** to the largest animal—does all of these things. There are just a few exceptions. Some special hybrid plants and animals (for example, mules, which cannot reproduce) may not have a given characteristic on this list.

Sometimes a nonliving thing will show one or more characteristics of a living thing, but that doesn't mean it is alive. For example, a car may use gasoline for "food," and a car's computer can help it respond to changes around it, but a car is not alive.

4. Why don't we think of a car as a living thing, even though it uses gasoline as "food" and can respond to changes around it?

_____

_____

_____

There are many ways to classify living things. Biologists (scientists who study living things) use characteristics such as how the organism looks, how it moves, how it reproduces, how it feeds or what it uses for food, and how it grows to classify plants and animals. For example, animals that have backbones are called **vertebrates**; animals that do not have backbones are called **invertebrates**.

5. Give three examples of vertebrates.

_____

_____

6. Which of the following is an invertebrate?
   A. a fish   C. an elephant
   B. a snake   D. an earthworm

Frogs and salamanders are **amphibians**.

7. List some characteristics of amphibians.

_____

_____

Beetles, grasshoppers, and mosquitoes are **insects**.

8. List some characteristics of insects.

_____

_____

Dogs, horses, and human beings are **mammals**.

9. List some characteristics of mammals.

_____

_____

The names that we use for plants and animals might lead you to think that all things by that name are exactly alike. But this is not so. For example, the term *bird* describes many different **species** of birds. Two different species of birds can be similar, but they are not exactly the same. This is why **biologists** (scientists who study living things) use several different characteristics of a plant or animal when classifying it.

10. An eagle and a chicken are both birds. How are they different?

_____

_____

Practice Questions

Directions: In the following illustration, icicles are growing from the edge of the roof. Use this information to answer Number 1.

1. What characteristics do the icicles share with living things?

_____

_____

_____

2. What characteristic do all birds share that allows them to be classified as birds?

   A. They all have webbed feet.

   B. They all have feathers.

   C. They all eat seeds.

   D. They all can fly.

3. Insects have three body parts, three pairs of legs, and antennae. Spiders are not classified as insects. Why is this?

   A. They have four pairs of legs.

   B. They have hairy bodies.

   C. They hatch their young.

   D. They spin webs.

4. Imagine that you have found a small, green, fuzzy clump of something. How could you tell whether the clump is made of living or nonliving material?

   _____

   _____

   _____

   _____

5. Which of the following is a vertebrate?

   A. a mouse

   B. a starfish

   C. a bacterium

   D. a grasshopper

Review 13

Basic Needs of Living Things

You know that people need certain things in order to survive—things like food, water, clean air, and shelter. Animals have the very same **basic needs**. They need to eat, drink, and breathe. They also need **shelter** from the weather, from natural disasters (such as hurricanes and floods), and from their enemies. Like people, animals have different ways of meeting these basic needs.

What Do You Think?

Think about how your family gets food.

1. What are some of your favorite foods that your family eats?

   _____

   _____

2. Where does this food come from?

   _____

   _____

3. How does it get to your house?

   _____

   _____

4. Where do you store the food that you do not eat right away?

   _____

   _____

Key Words

basic needs

shelter

Now think about a family of squirrels.

5. What foods do squirrels eat?

_____

_____

6. Where does a squirrel's food come from?

_____

_____

7. How do squirrels get their food?

_____

_____

8. What do squirrels do with the food that they do not want to eat right away?

_____

_____

What People Think

When you say, "I'm going home," what do you really mean? You probably mean that you are going to the house or apartment where you and your family eat, sleep, and keep all the things you own. Scientifically, you mean that you are going to the place that you use as shelter.

9. What are some things that your home shelters you from?

_____

_____

Different animals have different kinds of shelters. Animals use their shelters for a number of different things. Shelters protect animals from rain, wind, heat, and cold. They also protect animals from their enemies.

Like people, some animals build their own shelters. One animal that does this is the beaver. Beavers use the wood from trees they have cut down, along with rocks and mud, to build their shelters. These shelters, called *lodges*, are built in water. The inside area where the beavers live is above the surface level of the water. Small holes between the logs and branches in the ceiling let in fresh air. The entrances to the inside area are all below the surface of the water. This means that beavers have to swim to get home.

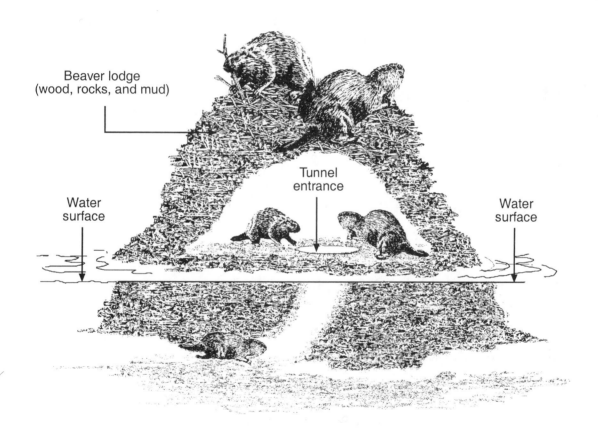

10. Why is the inside room of a beaver lodge above the surface of the water?
    A. because beavers should not spend much time in the water
    B. so that beavers can stay warm and dry when at home
    C. because beavers build lodges only in shallow water
    D. to make it easier to enter the lodge from the shore

11. How do you think having underwater entrances helps protect beavers from some of their enemies?

_____

_____

Not all animals build their own shelters. Bats and some bears, for example, use caves as shelters. Many snakes live in holes that other animals have left. Some kinds of fish use coral reefs or underwater plants as shelters.

Even though different animals have very different kinds of shelters, they all use the shelters for the same things. Shelters do more than keep animals comfortable and safe. They also give the animals a good place to raise their young.

Practice Questions

1. Which of the following is not a basic need of all animals?
   A. food
   B. clean air
   C. room to run around
   D. shelter from their enemies

2. How are eagles, sharks, and elephants alike?
   A. They all are mammals.
   B. They all have sharp teeth.
   C. They all are good swimmers.
   D. They all need water to survive.

3. Why do many wild animals live near a river, lake, or stream?

_____

_____

_____

_____

4. Why would clearing a forest to plant crops be harmful to the animals that live in the forest?

   A. There would not be enough shelter for the animals.

   B. There would be too much sunlight for the animals.

   C. There would not be enough water for the animals.

   D. There would be too much food for the animals.

5. All living things need food in order to continue living. Why, then, must you give food to a pet hamster, but you don't need to give food to a plant?

   A. Plants are not living things.

   B. Plants make their own food.

   C. Plants digest food from the air.

   D. Plants can live longer without food.

6. How are human beings' basic needs like the basic needs of beavers?

   _____

   _____

   _____

   _____

   How are human beings' basic needs different from beavers' basic needs?

   _____

   _____

   _____

   _____

Review 14

A Plant's Life

How many kinds of plants can you name? Do
the plants you can name look different from
each other? Are there any ways in which they are
alike? Even when plants look very different, they
still have some things in common. Most
important to remember is that all plants are
living things.

Key Words

flower

germination

leaf

life cycle

photosynthesis

reproduce

root

stem

What Do You Think?

Here is a bean seed.

1. Pretend that you are able to plant this seed. In the boxes below, draw
   what the seed will look like on Day 1, Day 15, and Day 30 after planting
   it in the soil. Remember to show the underground view, too.

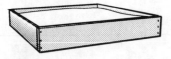

Bean Seed :
Day 1

Bean Seed :
Day 30

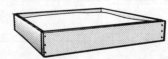

Bean Seed :
Day 15

What People Think

Every part of a plant does a special job to help that plant live and grow. Most plants have **roots**, **stems**, and **leaves**. Some plants even have **flowers**. Roots collect water and minerals from the soil. Stems carry the water and minerals to the leaves. The leaves use sunshine to make food for the plant. And flowers are important in helping plants **reproduce**, or make more plants.

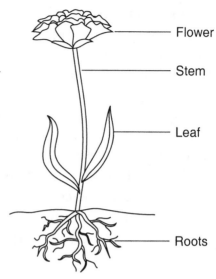

The roots, stems, and leaves are all important in helping the plant make food to live. The process that the plant uses to make food is called **photosynthesis**. The word *photosynthesis* might make more sense to you if you look at its parts. *Photo* means "light"; *synthesis* means "to put together or make." A plant makes its food using light.

2. What do you think would happen to plants if the sun did not shine for a long time?

   _____

   _____

   _____

Now you know how plants make food. How do they make more plants? One way that plants reproduce is by using flowers.

3. Make a list of at least five plants that have flowers.

   _____

   _____

   _____

Flowers do more than just look pretty and smell nice. The flower contains parts that allow the plant to reproduce. A flower's bright petals and nectar attract certain birds and insects, such as hummingbirds and honeybees. As the hummingbird or honeybee collects the nectar, it gets pollen on its body. The pollen rubs off when it goes to the flowers on the next plant. The pollen then helps that next plant make seeds.

4. Following is an incomplete diagram of the **life cycle** of a flowering plant. Complete the diagram by labeling the stages and processes of the life cycle. Write the correct terms in the empty boxes. The terms that you should use are: adult plant, young plant, seed, dead plant, **germination** (when the seeds sprout), reproduction, growth, and death.

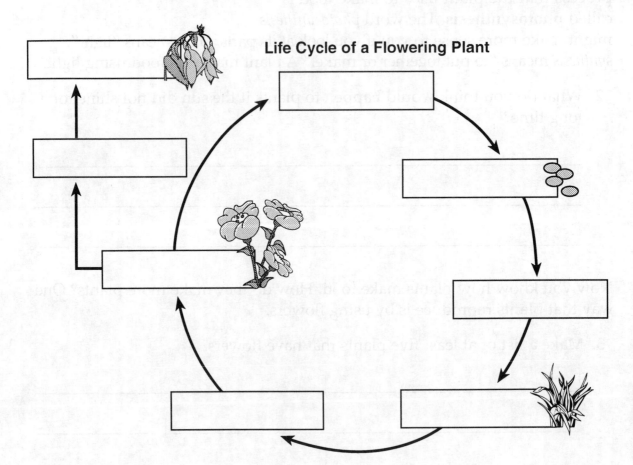

Life Cycle of a Flowering Plant

Practice Questions

1. In which part of a plant is food made?

   A. roots

   B. stem

   C. leaves

   D. flowers

2. In the story "Jack and the Beanstalk," what part of the bean plant grew toward the sky and helped Jack as he climbed up into the clouds?

   A. roots

   B. stem

   C. leaves

   D. flowers

3. Which part of a plant would be most important if a very strong wind started to blow?

   A. roots

   B. stem

   C. leaves

   D. flowers

4. The term for when a seed sprouts (starts to grow) is

   A. germination.

   B. implantation.

   C. reproduction.

   D. photosynthesis.

5. Mrs. Rumphius planted lupine seeds, and they grew into plants with beautiful flowers. She wanted to plant more seeds for the next year, but she was sick and could not go outside. The next spring, she was surprised to see that there were more flowers than ever. What do you think happened?

_____

_____

_____

_____

6. Planting seeds is not the only way to get new plants. How might a new plant be started without a seed? (Hint: Think about the other parts of a plant.)

_____

_____

_____

_____

PEOPLE IN SCIENCE

In 1883, Harriet Strong's husband died, and she was left with four children to support. Although she had a small farm in southern California, she knew nothing about farming the dry, desert-like land. She decided to teach herself. She studied which crops grew best in dry climates, and she invented a new way to water them. The U.S. government gave her an award for her new system. Then

Harriet W. R. Strong
(United States 1844–1929)

Congress decided to develop the area around the Grand Canyon. They wanted to use the Colorado River as a source of water for crops, and they thought of Strong. She talked to Congress twice to give them advice about the Colorado River project. Today, thanks to Strong's watering system, the Colorado River is an important source of water for southern California.

Review 15

From Generation to Generation

Animal life cycles are a lot like the plant life cycles that you learned about in Review 14. Animals live, grow, reproduce (create new animals), and die. The life cycle is how every species continues from one generation to the next. The life cycle also keeps each species from having too many members and overcrowding the earth. Read on to find out more about animal life cycles.

<table>
<tr><td colspan="2">Key Words</td></tr>
<tr><td colspan="2">extinct</td></tr>
<tr><td colspan="2">gene</td></tr>
<tr><td colspan="2">genetic information</td></tr>
<tr><td colspan="2">instinct</td></tr>
<tr><td colspan="2">learned</td></tr>
<tr><td colspan="2">metamorphosis</td></tr>
<tr><td colspan="2">offspring</td></tr>
<tr><td colspan="2">trait</td></tr>
<tr><td colspan="2">variation</td></tr>
</table>

What Do You Think?

In some families, the family members look very much alike. In other families, people might not look alike at all.

1. In the table that follows, list the members of your family, starting with yourself. Then describe the physical characteristics, or features, for each person.

Physical Characteristics of Family Members

Family Member	Hair Color	Hair Type	Eye Color
Me			

2. Which, if any, of these characteristics change naturally in a person?

_____

3. Write one physical characteristic that is similar for your family members.

_____

Write one physical characteristic that is different for your family members.

_____

What People Think

Every cell of every organism carries **genetic information**. Genetic information tells cells what kind of cell to be. For example, when a human baby is developing inside the mother, genetic information tells some cells to be skin cells, other cells to be brain cells, and so on. Genetic information also controls our physical **traits**, or how our bodies look. It controls what color our eyes and hair will be, how tall we grow, and many other traits.

4. Which of the following is not a trait that is controlled by genetic information?
   A. the shape of a person's nose
   B. the length of a person's fingers
   C. whether a person has short hair or long hair
   D. whether a person's hair grows straight or curly

As you can see from Number 4, some physical traits are caused by genetic information, but others are caused by choices we make. For example, people can decide to dye their hair purple, but they can't control what color it naturally grows.

A trait can also be something an organism does. If an organism is born knowing how to do something, that is an **instinct**. For example, a human infant is born with a sucking instinct. Other traits can be **learned**—the organism has to be taught how to do something. Young children, for example, must be taught how to feed themselves.

5. Imagine that you just got a new puppy. What instincts does your puppy have?

_____

_____

What things do you need to teach your puppy?

_____

_____

When an organism reproduces, or creates a new organism, the new organism is called **offspring**. All offspring get their genetic information from their parents. But if all offspring get their genetic information from their parents, why don't we all look just like our parents? It's because everyone has more genetic information than is actually used. For example, everyone has two pieces of genetic information, or **genes**, for eye color, but most people have two eyes that are the same color. Only one eye-color gene is "turned on." This means that if two parents have brown eyes, they could still have blue-eyed offspring if both parents carry a blue-eye gene. When offspring have traits that are different from their parents' traits, it is called **variation**.

6. How many different eye colors are there among the family members that you listed in the table earlier in this review?

_____

Each generation of species has to survive long enough to reproduce itself. Otherwise, that species disappears. For example, not every raccoon has to reproduce, but a whole group of raccoons has to produce enough healthy offspring to replace the raccoons that die from old age or other causes. When a species dies off faster than it reproduces, it becomes **extinct**—eventually, it no longer exists. In order to continue living from generation to generation, each species must have special ways to find food, find shelter, and create the next generation.

Organisms usually produce more than one offspring. This is because not all of the offspring that are produced will survive. If many are produced, there is a better chance that some will grow to adulthood.

7. About how many acorns (seeds) do you think an oak tree produces each year?

_____

About how many new oak trees sprout around the oak tree each year?

_____

Think about this: If every egg produced by every fly were somehow to survive to become an adult, within a couple of years the entire earth would be covered with a layer of flies about three feet deep!

You know that human beings change as they grow and age. Other animals change in even bigger ways. Sometimes these changes can be so big that it seems like the animal is turning into a different kind of living thing. The process of life cycle changes that are this big is called **metamorphosis**.

8. Which of the following organisms does not go through metamorphosis?
    A. frog
    B. chicken
    C. butterfly
    D. grasshopper

Practice Questions

1. The earth was formed nearly 4.5 billion years ago. Since that time, 99 percent of all the species that have ever lived on the earth have become extinct. What are some things that might cause a whole species to disappear?

_____

_____

_____

_____

2. Which of the following behaviors is an example of instinct?

    A. a cat using a litter box

    B. a chimpanzee using sign language

    C. a dog begging for food at the dinner table

    D. a male grasshopper rubbing its legs together to attract a female

3. Every little white fleck from a dried dandelion flower is a seed for another dandelion. Why are there so many dandelion seeds on each plant?

_____

_____

_____

_____

4. Look at the following diagram of a butterfly's life cycle. What is the science word for this kind of life cycle?

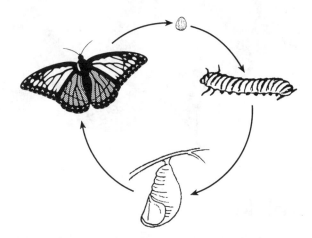

    A. variation   C. metamorphosis

    B. reproduction   D. genetic information

5. What is the science word for the baby of any kind of animal?

    A. gene   C. variation

    B. offspring   D. reproduction

Review 16

Living Things Adapt

Have you ever wondered why water rolls off a duck's back or why a frog's eyes bulge the way they do? The duck's feathers and the frog's eyes are features that help them to survive. All of the millions of different kinds of living things in the world have special features that help them to survive. Humans have special features, too. Some of these features are the ability to walk upright, thumbs on our hands, and a very high level of intelligence.

What Do You Think?

Think about the bears you have seen in books, on television, or maybe at the zoo. Different kinds of bears live in different places. Each different kind of bear has special features that help it to survive wherever it lives.

Key Words
adapt
adaptation
environment

1. Name the different bears that you have seen. What is special about them?

_____

_____

_____

2. Where do the bears that you have seen live?

_____

_____

_____

3. Could any of the bears survive if they switched where they lived with a different kind of bear? Why or why not?

_____

_____

_____

What People Think

When scientist Charles Darwin visited the Galapagos Islands in the 1830s, he found 14 species of birds called finches. Some species of finch ate seeds; others ate insects. Some of the seed-eating finches ate seeds found on the ground, others picked them out of cactus plants, and some did both. Darwin observed that each type of finch had its own type of beak. Each beak type was shaped for the type of food that finch species ate and the way it ate the food. The different beaks helped the different finches survive.

4. If a bird needed to eat seeds buried in the prickly spines of a cactus, what would be the best shape for its beak? In the following box, draw what this beak would look like.

Explain why you made the beak this shape.

_____

_____

_____

_____

You might think that any animal or plant can live in any place, but this is not true. The place where a plant or animal lives is its **environment**. All of the living and nonliving things in an organism's environment affect it. When an organism changes in a way that helps it to survive, we say that the organism has **adapted**. All organisms develop special features, or **adaptations**, that help them survive and meet their basic needs in their environment. Over time, each animal and plant becomes specially adapted, or fitted, to live in its particular environment. If the environment changes, the living things in it must also change. It usually takes many years and generations for a kind of organism to change.

5. What will most likely happen if an environment changes but a certain plant does not adapt?
    A. The plant will continue to live as it always has.
    B. The plant will start growing in a new place.
    C. The plant will become extinct.
    D. The plant will slowly change.

6. Here are some examples of special features of different plants and animals. How does each feature help the plant or animal survive?

Thorns on a rosebush: _____

A frog's sticky tongue: _____

A lion's claws: _____

The thumb on your hand: _____

Sometimes, offspring look different from their parents or from the other young. They may even act differently. You might think that being different is a bad thing. In nature, however, it is often a good thing. When there are differences among members of a species—when there is *variation*—the species has a better chance to survive. This is because the variations that make a certain member of the species different often help it to survive. As long as offspring of a species survive, the species continues to exist.

7. Some birds have very bright feathers that their enemies (predators) can easily see. Why are the offspring of these birds usually born with dull-colored feathers that blend into the background?

_____

_____

_____

Practice Questions

1. When living things adapt, they change so that they can better survive in their environment. Adaptation happens
   A. very quickly.
   B. somewhat quickly.
   C. somewhat slowly.
   D. very slowly.

2. Ducks' feet have webbing between the toes. How does this help ducks to survive?
   A. It helps them to paddle across water.
   B. It helps them catch food with their feet.
   C. It helps them to sit on branches in trees.
   D. It helps them attract a mate and have offspring.

3. Which of the following variations would probably help a baby bird to survive in the woods of the northern United States?
   A. having no feathers
   B. having very brightly colored feathers
   C. having fewer feathers than its brothers and sisters
   D. having feathers that blend in with the area where it lives

Directions: Use the following pictures to answer Number 4.

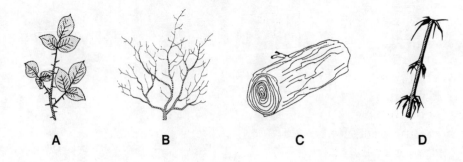

| A | B | C | D |

4. Which of these stems has the best defense against an animal eating its bark?
   A. A   C. C
   B. B   D. D

5. There are frogs in many parts of the world. Some have webbed feet; others have separated toes. What difference do you think this makes in the way these frogs live?

_____

_____

_____

_____

_____

PEOPLE IN SCIENCE

Constantine Rafinesque
(Turkey 1783–1840)

Constantine Rafinesque was born in Turkey, but his work took him all over the world. Rafinesque was a naturalist. He collected and studied newly discovered plants and animals. His collection was very large and included many one-of-a-kind specimens. Rafinesque was very careful with his collection. When he traveled, he took it with him. This caused him some problems. In 1815, his entire collection— 50 cases of specimens and equipment— was lost in a shipwreck in Long Island Sound. He had other troubles, too.

Rafinesque once caught and studied an octopus. When he had finished studying the squirmy creature, he cooked and ate it. Then he realized he didn't have another octopus like the one he had cooked for supper. He had just eaten his only example of this newly discovered species. It took 82 years for someone to find another one. Despite these setbacks, Constantine Rafinesque is given credit for discovering more than 100 plant and animal species, and he was the author of more than 950 publications.

Review 17

Healthy Humans

Keeping your body healthy is a lifelong task. You need to learn about what you can do to keep your body healthy when you are young. What you learn now will help you form good **health habits** for your future.

What Do You Think?

Look at the people below.

1. In order to have an active, healthy lifestyle, like the people in the pictures, what are some good health habits you need to have? List all the things you can think of that you can do to take good care of your body and stay healthy.

_____

_____

_____

_____

_____

_____

Key Words

balanced diet

food group

food guide pyramid

health habit

nutrient

What People Think

You can keep your body healthy in many ways. Remember, the healthy habits you form now will help you to have a healthy lifestyle in the future. Most health problems are preventable. That means you can do something to stop a problem before it starts. Brushing and flossing your teeth, for example, can prevent cavities. What you do each day to stay healthy is very important.

One important healthy habit is eating a **balanced diet**. A balanced diet gives our bodies all the **nutrients** they need to stay healthy and to grow. Nutrients are substances found in food that help our bodies. Nutrients include vitamins and minerals. The most important nutrient of all is water. Our bodies can live for several weeks without other nutrients, but we can live for only a week or so without water.

Sometimes it can be hard to know just what to eat in order to have a good, balanced diet. This is where the **food guide pyramid**, shown here, can help.

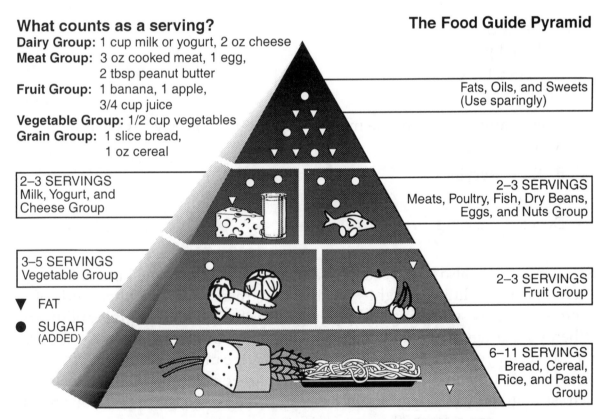

What counts as a serving?
Dairy Group: 1 cup milk or yogurt, 2 oz cheese
Meat Group: 3 oz cooked meat, 1 egg,
2 tbsp peanut butter
Fruit Group: 1 banana, 1 apple,
3/4 cup juice
Vegetable Group: 1/2 cup vegetables
Grain Group: 1 slice bread,
1 oz cereal

The Food Guide Pyramid

Fats, Oils, and Sweets
(Use sparingly)

2–3 SERVINGS
Milk, Yogurt, and
Cheese Group

2–3 SERVINGS
Meats, Poultry, Fish, Dry Beans,
Eggs, and Nuts Group

3–5 SERVINGS
Vegetable Group

2–3 SERVINGS
Fruit Group

▼ FAT

● SUGAR
(ADDED)

6–11 SERVINGS
Bread, Cereal,
Rice, and Pasta
Group

U.S. DEPT. OF AGRICULTURE GUIDE TO DAILY FOOD CHOICES

2. What does the food guide pyramid tell you about the foods you should
   eat?

   _____

   _____

   _____

3. List the **food groups** that are shown on the food guide pyramid.

   _____

   _____

   _____

4. Apples are part of which food group?
   A. fruit group
   B. dairy group
   C. bread group
   D. vegetable group

5. How many servings of the meat group should you have every day?
   A. 1 to 2 servings
   B. 2 to 3 servings
   C. 3 to 5 servings
   D. 5 to 7 servings

Regular exercise also is important in a healthy lifestyle. Some kinds of
exercise, such as lifting weights, mostly strengthen muscles. Other kinds of
exercise, such as swimming and jogging, also strengthen the lungs and heart.
When your lungs are healthy, they do a better job of getting oxygen to your
blood. When your heart is healthy and strong, it can do a better job of
pumping blood and carrying oxygen to all parts of your body. In order to
help strengthen your lungs and heart, you should exercise so that your heart
pumps faster for at least 20 minutes at a time.

6. Which of the following would not be good exercise for your heart and lungs?

   A. running a mile

   B. dancing in a ballet class

   C. playing basketball with a friend

   D. practicing hitting a target with a bow and arrow

If you eat a balanced diet and get regular exercise, chances are good that your body will stay healthier. It will be able to repair damage from germs and injuries, it will be able to grow well, and your weight will be in a healthy range—not too thin and not overweight. The food energy you eat should match the amount of energy you use. Practice good health habits!

Practice Questions

1. Good health habits should be learned when a person is

   A. an adult.   C. young.

   B. a parent.   D. sick.

2. What is meant by *a balanced diet*?

   A. weighing food before eating it

   B. eating food from each of the main food groups

   C. eating the same weight of each kind of food per meal

   D. having only one helping of the main dish and one of dessert

3. How does exercise improve the muscles of the body?

   A. It makes them relax.

   B. It makes them longer.

   C. It makes them stronger.

   D. It makes them lose weight.

4. Why is getting enough sleep important for a person's health?

   A. It allows your body to recover from daily activity.

   B. It gives your body time to digest what you eat.

   C. It helps conserve heat, electricity, and food.

   D. It lets a person have dreams.

5. The most important nutrient for humans is

 A. meat.

 B. water.

 C. calcium.

 D. vitamin C.

6. What is the best way to get all of the nutrients your body needs?

 A. Take vitamins.

 B. Grow your own food.

 C. Pick one food from each food group to eat most of the time.

 D. Eat many different kinds of food from each of the food groups.

PEOPLE IN SCIENCE

Ana de Osorio,
Countess of Cinchon
(Spain 17th century)

Centuries ago, people from Europe started to explore the world. They traveled all over, but one thing kept getting in their way: malaria. Malaria is a serious disease spread by a certain kind of mosquito. It was dangerous for explorers to travel where malaria was found. This included most tropical countries and the swamplands of North America. Today, thanks to Ana de Osorio, the Countess of Cinchon, malaria does not stop people from circling the globe. In 1638, the countess was living in the South American country of Peru. She caught malaria but was cured after taking a medicine that native people made from tree bark. The countess was not a trained scientist, but she thought like a scientist. She understood that this bark was a cure for malaria. She brought the bark back to her home in Spain and convinced doctors to use it. The bark was named "cinchona" in honor of the countess. The bark is the source of quinine. Quinine has been used around the world to treat malaria since the countess introduced it to Spanish doctors in the 1600s.

Review 18

Growth and Healing

Have you ever watched a plant grow? You may have noticed that many plants grow from the tips of their stems or roots. Many plants also produce buds that become leaves or flowers. Can you imagine how silly you would look if you grew from the tips of your fingers, toes, or the top of your head? You would begin to look very strange indeed! But how *do* you grow? And how does your body fix itself when you have a cut, a bruise, or a broken bone? Read on to find out more.

What Do You Think?

Have you ever looked at your baby pictures from just after you were born? They might make you laugh a little, but it is pretty amazing how much you have changed since then.

1. Maybe you do not remember exactly how long you were when you were born, but make a good estimate, and write it down.

   Length at birth: _____

   What is your length (height) now? _____

   About how much have you grown since you were a baby? _____

2. Do you think that your cells get bigger as you grow, or does the number of cells in your body increase? Give at least one reason for your answer.

   _____

   _____

   _____

Key Words

calcium

clot

protein

What People Think

Some people do very odd things to get their names in *The Guinness Book of Records*. For example, a person from the United States spent 12 years growing fingernails that were 17 1/4 inches long. You can imagine how difficult it would be to do things with fingernails that long—think about trying to wash your hair! And speaking of hair, the longest hair in the world has grown to 16 feet 10 inches over 70 years.

Your fingernails are made of a **protein** (molecules that help build our bodies) called *keratin*, and they are always growing. Most people's fingernails grow 0.5 to 1.2 millimeters each day. You may want to find a ruler to check out how long this is.

3. You should always have a balanced diet, but which of the following foods is most helpful in keeping your fingernails healthy?

   A. meat

   B. candy

   C. lettuce

   D. french fries

Besides eating good foods to stay healthy, you also need to practice other good health habits—things like brushing your teeth and taking a shower.

4. Do you think it is a good health habit to have very long fingernails? What are two good health habits that you should practice to take care of your nails?

   _____

   _____

Like your fingernails, your hair also is made of keratin. Each hair on your head grows for about three years and then rests for one or two years.

5. Do you think that all of your hairs rest at one time, or do they take turns resting? Give at least one reason why you think so.

   _____

   _____

If you scrape your knee, it probably hurts, and it probably begins to bleed. If the scrape is not too deep, it eventually stops bleeding because your blood begins to **clot**. When the blood has finished clotting, there is a scab over the scrape. Blood clotting and wound healing are complicated processes. The first thing that happens after you get a cut or scrape is that a protein net begins to form over the wound.

6. Think about where you use a net or screen and why you use that net or screen. What do you think the protein net over a wound does? (Hint: Blood is made of several different kinds of cells.)

_____

_____

7. If you get a deep cut, why would you probably need stitches?

_____

_____

8. If you do not keep a cut clean, what can happen to the cut?

_____

9. Which of the following is not a sign that a cut is infected?
   A. The person has a slight fever.
   B. There is pus coming from the cut.
   C. The skin around the cut is its normal color.
   D. The skin around the cut is sore and swollen.

10. If a cut becomes infected, what are two things that you could do to help the cut heal? (You should tell someone who can help you, but there are also some things that you could do yourself.)

_____

_____

In Review 17, you learned about nutrients. **Calcium** is one nutrient that does many things in the body. It helps your bones and teeth grow, your muscles and nerves work, and your blood clot. It is important to have enough calcium in your diet. Persons age four and over should get at least 900 milligrams (about 0.03 ounces) of calcium every day. This is the amount of calcium in about three-and-a-half cups of yogurt.

11. List three foods besides yogurt that are good sources of calcium.

Practice Questions

1. Bones need calcium and vitamins C and D to grow well. Which of the following lists the best sources for calcium and vitamins C and D?

    A. orange juice, milk, and eggs   C. bread, milk, and green beans

    B. peanut butter, milk, and rice   D. potato chips, milk, and water

2. If a bone breaks, a blood clot forms by the break, then blood vessels form and grow in the area. Which of the following is the best reason this happens?

    A. The blood vessels protect the break area.

    B. The blood vessels carry the injured cells away.

    C. The blood vessels grow because there is now room for them.

    D. The blood vessels carry things to the break that help repair it.

3. Which of the following is the best proof that your hair is not living?

    A. You can wash your hair.

    B. You can change your hair color.

    C. You can cut your hair without feeling pain.

    D. You can grow your hair long if you want to.

4. If you get a small cut, which of the following is best to do first?

    A. Immediately put some antibiotic ointment in the cut.

    B. Immediately wash the cut with clean water and soap.

    C. Immediately cover the cut with a clean bandage.

    D. Immediately call the doctor for help.

5. You may know about the 911 system that you call on the phone in emergencies, but did you know that your cells have their own "911" system? Instead of phone lines, your body uses chemical messages to signal where help is needed. These chemical signals cause cells and other materials in your body to arrive at the scene of the "accident" to help fix the trouble.

   a) Think back to when you have gotten a small cut or scrape. Describe two things that you have observed just after you were cut. Then describe two things you observed as the cut began to heal.

   _____

   _____

   _____

   _____

   b) Describe at least two things that your body has to do to help repair the cut.

   _____

   _____

   _____

   _____

6. When a person breaks a bone, a cast is often placed around the break. The doctor often wants the person to stay in bed or not move a lot at first. Why do you think it is important to put on a cast and not move much during the first few days after the break?

   _____

   _____

   _____

   _____

Review 19

The Web of Life

Think of the last time you helped somebody do something. Maybe you helped your family by washing the dinner dishes. Maybe you helped a younger child cross the street. Or maybe you helped a friend understand a new idea in math. We are always helping each other. In this review, you'll think some more about how all living things help each other.

What Do You Think?

How do you get to school in the morning? Do you walk? Do you ride the bus? Do you ride a bike? Get a ride in a car? Do you have to rely on any other people in order to get to school?

1. On the line below, write down how you get to school in the morning.

   _____

2. Now think about whether or not you have to rely on any other people in order to get to school. On the lines below, write down every single person you can think of who helped make it possible for you to get to school in the morning.

   _____

   _____

   _____

   _____

   _____

3. How many people are in your list?

   _____

Key Words
food chain
food web
predator
prey

What People Think

When you stopped to think about it, you probably realized that there are many people who helped make it possible for you to get to school this morning. Even if you simply walked from your home, there are many people who helped. There are people who built the sidewalks and people who made the concrete; there are people who planned where the streets would go and people who installed stoplights; there are people who created the fabrics in your clothes and people who made an umbrella for a rainy day. The list could go on and on and on.

Just as you couldn't get to school without the work of many people, most of whom you will never even know, all living things depend on one another in order to live. In Review 14, you learned about photosynthesis, in which plants use carbon dioxide in the air to make their food and also to give off oxygen into the air. Animals, on the other hand, breathe in the oxygen, eat the food, and then breathe out carbon dioxide for the plants to use again.

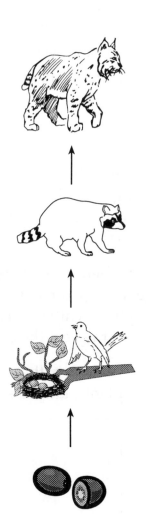

Carbon is a substance that goes in a cycle from plants to animals and back again. Let's look at the carbon cycle. Start with a bird that laid an egg. Many birds like fruit, so let's imagine that the mother bird eats a kiwi fruit before laying the egg. Some of the carbon in the kiwi becomes part of the mother bird, and some of this carbon then becomes part of the egg.

Another animal—let's say a raccoon—comes along and gobbles up the egg. Now the carbon has passed from the kiwi to the mother bird, to the egg, and then to the raccoon.

But it doesn't end there. A bobcat in the neighborhood finds the raccoon a tasty snack. What happens to the kiwi's carbon now? It becomes a part of the bobcat.

These food connections are called a **food chain**. We could draw a kiwi-to-bobcat food chain as in the diagram at the right.

Animals that eat other animals are **predators**. Predators are shown at the tips of the arrows. They eat the animals at the tails of the arrows, the **prey**. In real life, food chains have branches that make **food webs**. For example, other animals might also eat birds' eggs. Some snakes eat eggs. Hawks eat snakes. This means we could add another food chain for a snake and a hawk. Now we have a food web that looks like the diagram at the right.

4. Which of the following is the best term to use to describe all of the living things in a forest?

   A. prey
   B. predators
   C. food web
   D. food chain

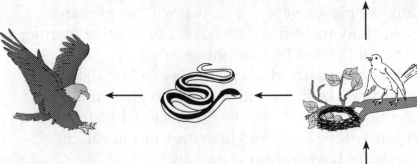

When carbon passes along the food web, energy is also being passed along. Living things get energy by combining the carbon in their food with oxygen (a process called *respiration*).

But where does energy come from in the first place? Plants are the key: Plants get energy directly from sunlight and use the sun's energy to make their food in photosynthesis. This sun and food energy is then passed along to animals when they eat the plants.

5. In the box that follows, draw a food web for a pond that has water plants, tadpoles, small fish, big fish, ducks, and insects.

Practice Questions

Directions: Use the following illustration to answer Numbers 1 through 3.

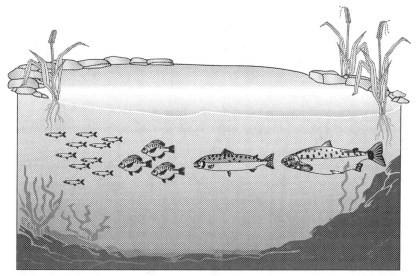

Left   **Right**

1. What is the source of energy for this food web?

    A. water

    B. soil

    C. sun

    D. air

2. Look at the underwater part of the illustration. In what direction is energy being moved among the organisms?

    A. left to right

    B. right to left

    C. bottom to top

    D. top to bottom

3. Which of the following statements best describes the relationship between the big and small fish?

    A. The big fish are prey and the small fish are predators.

    B. The small fish are prey and the big fish are predators.

    C. The big fish and the small fish are in different food webs.

    D. The small fish are predators and the big fish are lower in the food chain.

Directions: Use the following diagram to answer Numbers 4 and 5.

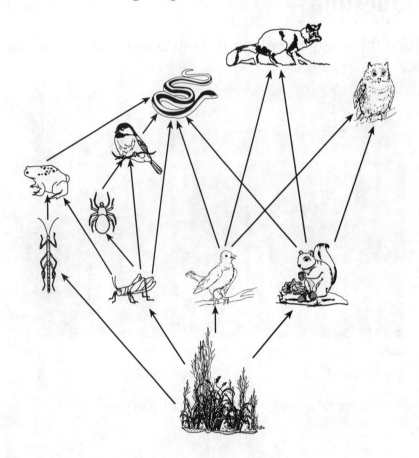

4. What do all of the animals shown have in common?

    A. They eat plants.

    B. They eat other animals.

    C. They give the plants energy.

    D. They breathe out carbon dioxide.

5. Imagine that the bird in the center of the food web (between the grasshopper and the squirrel) suddenly died out. Explain what you think would happen to the rest of the food web if this bird were no longer there.

_____

_____

_____

_____

Review 20

Nature Recycles

It seems as if everywhere you look, a sign tells you to **recycle**. Maybe there is even a truck that comes to pick up recyclable materials from your home to be reused. Why is everyone so concerned with recycling? One reason is because there are only so many materials on Earth. If we use them all only once, we will run out very quickly. Nature recycles itself all the time. For example, when a plant dies, other living things break down the parts of the plant so that it becomes part of the soil. The material from the plant that has died is then used to help new plants grow. Human beings should learn from the rest of nature, which has been around for much longer than we have. Everything in nature is recycled again and again.

Key Words

carnivore

consumer

decomposer

herbivore

nonrenewable
   resource

omnivore

producer

recycle

renewable resource

What Do You Think?

Take a few minutes to think about the things you recycle and the things you *could* recycle.

1. What are some non-food items that you use just once? List them below.

    _____

    _____

2. What items from your list could you use again? How could you use them?

    _____

    _____

3. What is the main reason for recycling things like cans, bottles, newspapers, and so on?

    _____

    _____

What People Think

You know that all living things have basic needs: food, water, clean air, and shelter. These needs have to be met by the environment. Some things in the environment are renewed naturally—plants grow and replace other plants all the time, for example. Because plants can grow and be renewed fairly quickly, we think of them as **renewable resources**. A *resource* is something in nature that living things use to live and survive.

On the other hand, Earth is making new soil all the time, but it may take 100,000 years to make just a few inches of new soil. It takes Earth a few million years to make a new deposit of coal or oil. From the point of view of humans, therefore, these resources are **nonrenewable**. What we have of these resources here on Earth now is all that we will ever have, at least for hundreds of thousands or millions of years.

4. Is wood a renewable or nonrenewable resource?

    _____

Explain why you think this.

_____

_____

Recycling happens every day in nature through the food chain. As you know, living things depend on other living things for survival. A useful way to think of living things is to separate them into two groups: **producers** and **consumers**. The producers are the plants. Plants change energy from the sun into food. Plants are needed by the primary consumers: the animals who eat only plants. These animals are called **herbivores**. The herbivores are needed by the secondary consumers: the animals who eat meat. These animals are called **carnivores**. Some species, including humans, eat both plants and meat; these species are called **omnivores**.

5. Which of the following would an omnivore eat?
   A. meat   C. berries
   B. grass   D. all of the above

Decomposers are recyclers. They break down dead plants and animals into smaller pieces that can be used again by livings things to grow. For example, some decomposers, such as mushrooms, grow on rotting logs and help break them down. Living creatures aren't the only important things in our environment. The environment is made up of living and nonliving things. Living things include plants, fungi, microscopic organisms, bacteria, and viruses. Nonliving things include the air, soil, water, rocks, and things humans have built. The living organisms in an environment depend on the nonliving things in order to survive. For example, we sure couldn't live long without clean air or water!

6. Look back over the lists you made in the "What Do You Think?" section. Now divide them into two categories: those that are made from living things and those made from nonliving things.

   Made from living things: _____

   _____

   Made from nonliving things: _____

   _____

Practice Questions

Directions: The following picture shows living things that are part of a field food web. This food web is made up of three different food chains. Hawks and snakes eat only meat; mice eat only corn; and crickets eat both grasses and corn. Use this information to answer Numbers 1 through 3.

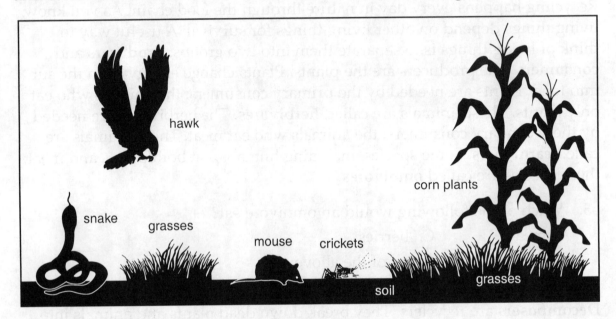

1. What are the producers in this diagram?

    A. soil, corn plants, and grasses

    B. grasses and corn plants

    C. the corn plants only

    D. the grasses only

2. Which of the following is an example of a food chain in the picture?

    A. The corn and the grasses grow in the soil.

    B. The snake and the mouse hide in the grasses.

    C. The mouse eats the corn, and the crickets eat the corn.

    D. The mouse eats the corn, and the hawk eats the mouse.

3. What animals compete for the same food?

    A. the hawk and the snake

    B. the hawk and the mouse

    C. the hawk and the crickets

    D. the snake and the crickets

Directions: Use the following diagram to answer Numbers 4 and 5. The jar in the diagram is closed, but the lid has air holes. No other food or materials are added to the environment in the jar, but sunlight can shine through the glass. There are plants growing at the bottom of the jar.

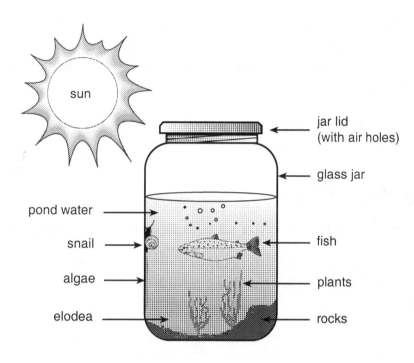

4. Which of the following is a consumer in the jar environment?

   A. plants
   B. water
   C. snail
   D. rocks

5. Why is sunlight important to the survival of the living things in this system?

   _____

   _____

   _____

6. Which of the following is a nonrenewable resource?

   A. oil
   B. cows
   C. wind
   D. wheat

Review 21

Humans and the World Around Us

There are some days when you don't spend much time outside in nature. You sleep inside. You might ride to school on a bus or in a car. You spend most of your day inside at school, and then you might get a ride back home and stay inside. You might start to think that we don't really need nature.

But wait. Could we really survive without the natural world? In this review, you'll think about why it is so important to take good care of our world.

What Do You Think?

Think some more about a day that you spent almost completely indoors.

1. How is the natural world important even on a day that you spend inside? You might start by thinking about the things you use that are from nature.

_____

_____

_____

_____

What People Think

Food is one thing you probably listed when you wrote about how the natural world is important even on a day when you stay inside. Food doesn't magically appear in the refrigerator or oven, and people can't just make it; it comes from a plant or animal in nature. You might have also listed fuels like oil and coal used to create heat or electricity. Oil and coal come from plants and animals that have died and decayed over millions of years. Food and oil are examples of **natural resources**, things found in nature that humans use.

Key Words

natural resource

pollution

technology

2. Which of the following is not a natural resource?

A. fish

B. gold

C. a spoon

D. wood for building

Our environment is all the living and nonliving things around us. It is important to take care of the environment and not waste any natural resources. People often make changes in their environment without meaning to harm it. But changing the natural environment usually has both good and bad effects—for nonliving things and for living things, including humans.

Imagine the Midwest in the early 1800s. Different kinds of grasses, some growing six feet tall, covered the landscape. As some grasses died and decayed, rich soil was formed and was kept in place by the deep grass roots. The grasses were so thick that not many trees grew except near streams and rivers. As more and more people came to live in the Midwest, they began plowing the prairie for farmland. As new and better tools were invented, it became easier for humans to plow more and more land.

3. List both good and bad effects that changing the prairie has had for living things, including humans.

_____

_____

_____

People can change the environment by doing things to it such as plowing or building on it. Unfortunately, we can also pollute it. **Pollution** is any harmful thing that causes the environment to become unhealthy. We can pollute the air, water, soil—just about anything. With more and more people living on the earth, it is more and more important to be careful not to pollute the environment.

4. List at least three ways cars can pollute the environment.

_____

_____

_____

Technology is anything that someone makes to help do something or to solve a problem. But whenever a new technology is created, it is important to think about how that technology might harm or pollute the environment.

5. Suppose that a certain insect has been eating corn plants so that none of the farmers in an area are able to grow corn to sell. Then, someone invents a powder that can be sprayed on the corn plant and that will kill the insect. How might the powder pollute the environment?

_____

_____

_____

Practice Questions

1. If there is a change in their environment, plants might do any of the following except which one?

    A. die

    B. grow

    C. adjust to the changes

    D. move to another area

2. Which of the following statements is true?

    A. All living things cause changes in the environment.

    B. Living things rarely change the environment.

    C. Changes in the environment are always bad.

    D. Only humans change the environment.

3. When humans change their environment, they usually don't mean to cause harm, but often there is harm anyway. This harm is sometimes because of

    A. bad weather that changes the environment.

    B. poor planning for cold winters and hot summers.

    C. not using enough natural resources while making changes.

    D. not thinking about what might happen to the environment.

4. Which of the following is a natural resource?

   A. a toothpick

   B. a pizza

   C. a river

   D. a hat

5. If your town decided to build a new park, how might it affect the environment? List at least three ways building the park might affect the environment.

   _____

   _____

   _____

   _____

   _____

PEOPLE IN SCIENCE

Rachel Carson
(United States 1907–1964)

Rachel Carson gave up writing so she could study science. Her teachers warned her that science was a man's world and that she should continue to write. Carson believed, however, that she had important work to do as a scientist. She went to college and studied the sea and sea life. Then she got a job at the U. S. Bureau of Fisheries. Her first task was to write about ocean life—her love of nature had led her full circle. From that time on, she used both her knowledge of science and her skills as a writer. In 1958, she took on a new challenge. She wrote about the effects of poisonous insect spray on the environment. She wondered what happened to the pesticide after it was sprayed onto our fields and forests. Did it disappear harmlessly, or, over time, did it kill organisms other than insects? Her book, *Silent Spring*, was the world's first warning about the deadly effects of chemical pesticides on the environment. When it was published in 1962, tens of thousands of people read her book, and President Kennedy ordered further study of pesticides. Thanks to Carson's efforts, we now have laws to protect our environment from dangerous chemicals.

Activity 8

Comparing Living Things

In Review 12, you learned that scientists put things into groups so that it is easier to study them. This activity will give you practice at doing the same thing that scientists do.

Using What You Know

Think about the living organisms shown in and around the pond below.

Step 1: Put all the living things into two categories: plants and animals.

Plants: _____

_____

Animals: _____

_____

Step 2: Separate the animals into two groups: vertebrates and invertebrates.

Vertebrates: _____

_____

Invertebrates: _____

_____

Step 3: Separate the animals into two groups: those who lay eggs and those who give birth to live young.

Lay eggs: _____

_____

Give birth to live young: _____

_____

Think It Over

1. How are the vertebrates at the pond different from the other animals?

   _____

   _____

   _____

2. In what ways are an earthworm and a snake alike? In what ways are they different?

   _____

   _____

   _____

3. Describe the life cycle of a frog.

   _____

   _____

   _____

4. Where would you most likely find frog eggs in or around a pond? Where would you most likely find tadpoles? Where would you probably find adult frogs?

   Eggs: _____

   Tadpoles: _____

   Frogs: _____

Activity 9

Are Your Earlobes Attached?

Instincts are inherited traits passed by the parents to their offspring. Other traits are inherited, too. In this activity, you will explore some of the physical traits that humans inherit from their parents.

Using What You Know

Work with one or two partners to study five traits of the people in your classroom.

Step 1: The five traits you should study are shown in the illustrations. Collect data about each trait and record your data in the tables that follow Step 1. Put a tally mark in the correct box for each piece of information that you gather. Keep separate records for boys and for girls.

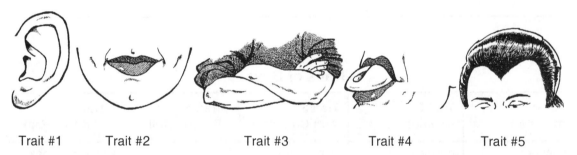

Trait #1   Trait #2   Trait #3   Trait #4   Trait #5

Trait 1: earlobes—Check everyone's earlobes to see if they are attached or unattached.

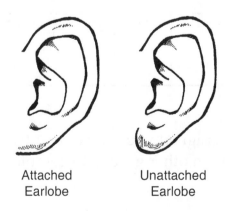

Attached
Earlobe

Unattached
Earlobe

Trait 2: dimples—Check everyone for little dents in the chin or cheeks.

Trait 3: arm crossing—Have everyone fold their arms across their chests and note which arm is on top.

Trait 4: tongue rolling—See if people can curl the edges of their tongues upward.

Trait 5: widow's peak—Check for a downward point in the middle of the hairline on the forehead. If the hairline goes straight across the top of the forehead, it is not a widow's peak.

Traits of Girls

Trait 1: Earlobes	Trait 2: Dimples	Trait 3: Arm Crossing	Trait 4: Tongue Rolling	Trait 5: Widow's Peak
attached:	dimples:	right over left:	can roll:	widow's peak:
unattached:	no dimples:	left over right:	cannot roll:	no widow's peak:

Traits of Boys

Trait 1: Earlobes	Trait 2: Dimples	Trait 3: Arm Crossing	Trait 4: Tongue Rolling	Trait 5: Widow's Peak
attached:	dimples:	right over left:	can roll:	widow's peak:
unattached:	no dimples:	left over right:	cannot roll:	no widow's peak:

Step 2: If your teacher assigned you only one or two traits to research, exchange data with other groups to complete your tables.

Think It Over

1. Which trait(s) is (are) the same for most students in your classroom?

   _____

   _____

   Does your data show any differences between boys and girls for these traits? If so, which traits?

   _____

   _____

   _____

   _____

2. What is one feature of your physical appearance that is not a trait that can be inherited from your parents?

   _____

3. How might something like the size or position of an animal's ears help or hurt its chances for survival?

   _____

   _____

4. What kind of special trait would help an animal survive in a place that has a lot of soft, marshy ground?

   _____

   _____

Activity 10

Built for Survival

Every living thing on Earth has to adapt, or adjust, to the place where it lives so that it can survive. For example, you have learned that birds' beaks are different shapes, depending on what kind of food they eat. A pelican's beak has a big pouch so that it can hold the fish it catches, whereas a hummingbird's beak is long and very thin so that it can fit deep inside flowers. Plants develop different features, too. This activity will give you a chance to study some of them.

Using What You Know

Your teacher will show you which plants to study.

Step 1: Every kind of plant on Earth has characteristics that help it live in its environment. Look closely at the three plants your teacher has shown you.

In the space below, draw the plants you have observed.

How are the leaves on the three plants different from each other?

_____

_____

_____

_____

Step 2: Your teacher will direct you to three more plants. In the boxes provided here, draw the bark (the outer covering of the stem) of each plant.

Plant 1	Plant 2	Plant 3

Write down how the bark of each plant is different from the others.

Plant 1 bark is different because _____

_____

Plant 2 bark is different because _____

_____

Plant 3 bark is different because _____

_____

Think It Over

Directions: Use the following drawings of leaves to answer Numbers 1 through 5.

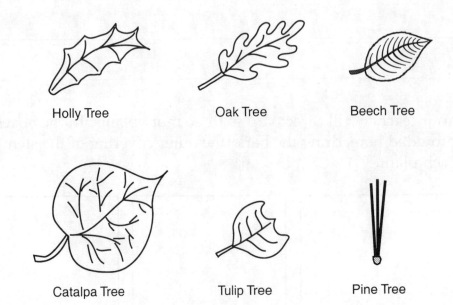

Holly Tree   Oak Tree   Beech Tree

Catalpa Tree   Tulip Tree   Pine Tree

1. What is one special thing about each of these leaves?

   Holly tree: _____

   Oak tree: _____

   Beech tree: _____

   Catalpa tree:_____

   Tulip tree: _____

   Pine tree:_____

2. How would hard, sharp points on leaves help a plant survive?

   _____

   _____

3. Study the drawings and decide how the leaves could be organized into two groups. Place the names of the leaves into these groups on the lines that follow.

Group 1: _____

_____

Group 2: _____

_____

4. What adaptations do the leaves of Group 1 have to help a plant survive?

_____

_____

_____

5. Decide which is your favorite leaf drawing (holly, oak, beech, catalpa, tulip, or pine). What special adaptation does the leaf have to help the plant survive?

_____

_____

_____

Activity 11

Neighborhood Web of Life

For this activity, you will need to review some key words.

producer: a plant (makes its own food)

primary consumer: an animal that eats plants (a *herbivore*)

secondary consumer: an animal that eats primary consumers (a *carnivore*) or that eats primary consumers and plants (an *omnivore*)

Using What You Know

Step 1: Look out a window. Draw a picture and/or write the names of all the plants you see that are framed by the window. Place them in the box labeled "Producers."

Producers	Primary Consumers	Secondary Consumers

Step 2: Look out the window again. Now add to your drawing or list all the herbivores you see. Put these animals in the box labeled "Primary Consumers."

Step 3: Look out the window one more time. Now add any carnivores you see outside the window. Put these animals in the box labeled "Secondary Consumers."

Step 4: If any of the carnivores also eat plants, put them in the box labeled "Primary Consumers" so you can see the total number of animals that eat plants for at least part of their diet.

Now look at the following three-level chart.

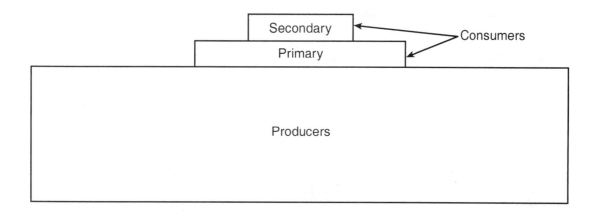

Why do you think the box for producers is so much bigger than the other boxes?

_____

_____

_____

Why do you think the secondary consumers box is so small?

_____

_____

_____

Think It Over

1. Why do you think primary consumers are called *herbivores*?

    _____

    _____

2. Why do herbivores have flat teeth?

    _____

    _____

3. Secondary consumers (carnivores) have sharp teeth or beaks. Why is this?

    _____

    _____

4. Look at your drawing or list in Step 1 and think about the scene outside your window. What living things are the decomposers, producers, and consumers in the school yard? List them below.

    Decomposers: _____

    _____

    Producers: _____

    _____

    Consumers: _____

    _____

5. Where do you and your family fit into this list? Why?

_____

_____

6. In the following box, draw a diagram of a food web for the organisms
   you drew or listed in the boxes after Step 1.

Activity 12

Chemical Spill

Chemicals are all around us. For example, as you read this paragraph, you are sitting in a sea of nitrogen, oxygen, and carbon dioxide gas. Many chemicals found in the environment are necessary for life. Many other chemicals have been discovered or created by humans. We use these chemicals for many purposes, such as to clean things and to manufacture things. If people are not careful, dangerous chemicals can get into the environment. This can pollute nonliving things in the environment—such as water, air, and soil—and can hurt or kill living things such as plants and animals. You will find out more about how a chemical spill works in this activity.

Using What You Know

You will work with a partner to investigate what may happen when a chemical is spilled. Your teacher will give you food coloring—your "chemical"—a ruler, and a small clear cup filled with dry sand.

Step 1: Place one drop of food coloring "chemical" in the center of the dry sand. Wait and observe for five minutes.

Describe and measure what happens.

_____

_____

_____

Step 2: Now sprinkle some water on your sand to see what can happen when rain falls on a chemical spill. Wait and observe for another five minutes.

Describe and measure what happens.

_____

_____

_____

Think It Over

1. What did you learn about chemical pollution in this activity?

   _____

   _____

   _____

2. What can you learn from this activity about cleaning up chemical spills in soil?

   _____

   _____

   _____

3. What are some other ways that chemical pollution can spread?

   _____

   _____

   _____

4. What is the easiest and least expensive way to keep the environment clean?

   _____

   _____

   _____

Appendix

Glossary

accurate   when something, such as a measurement or observation, is as exact as possible (Review 4)

adapt   to change in a way that helps a species to survive; it usually takes a long time and many generations for organisms to adapt (Review 16)

adaptation   a special characteristic of an organism that helps it survive and reproduce in its environment (Review 16)

air pressure   the force created by the weight of a column of air (Review 10)

amphibian   an animal that lives part of its life in water and part on land (Review 12)

atmosphere   the layer of gases surrounding the earth that helps support life (Review 10)

atom   a tiny particle that, combined with many other atoms, makes up all matter (Review 5)

axis   the imaginary line that runs through the earth from the North Pole to the South Pole (Review 9)

balanced diet   a diet that gives your body all the nutrients it needs to stay healthy and to grow (Review 17)

bar graph   a picture used to compare data that can be put into separate groups (Review 3)

basic needs   things that all living creatures must have in order to live: food, water, clean air, and shelter (Review 13)

biologist   a scientist who studies living things (Review 12)

calcium   a nutrient that helps your bones and teeth grow, your muscles and nerves work, and your blood clot (Review 18)

carnivore   an animal that eats meat (Review 20)

chemical change   when matter changes so that it is a new substance that behaves in ways that are different from the ways the original substance behaved (Review 5)

chemical energy   the energy that objects have because of the way their atoms are connected together (Review 6)

chemical property	a feature of matter that can be observed only by changing one kind of matter into another (Review 5)
circle graph	a picture that shows how much of a whole a certain part represents; also called a pie chart (Review 3)
circuit	a system of electrical parts (Review 6)
claim	a statement that someone wants us to believe is true (Review 4)
classify	to use characteristics to describe how things are alike or different (Review 12)
clot	to change from liquid blood to thicker blood that eventually stops the blood flow out of a wound (Review 18)
condensation	the process in which water vapor changes into a liquid (Review 10)
conservation of energy	energy is never created or destroyed; it only changes form (Review 6)
consumer	an animal that eats plants or other animals (Review 20)
data	information that describes events or things, such as temperatures or life spans (Review 2)
data table	a way to organize information into rows and columns (Review 2)
decomposer	a living organism that breaks down dead organisms into smaller parts that can be reused by other living organisms (Review 20)
electrical energy	the energy that causes charged particles to move through wires (Review 6)
energy	the ability to make something move or change (Review 6)
environment	all the living and nonliving things that surround and affect a living thing (Review 16)
erosion	when small particles of soil and rock are broken down and carried away by glaciers, water, or wind (Review 11)
error	an incorrect measurement or observation (Review 2)

estimate	a judgment or rough calculation made without measurement (Review 2)
evaluate	to think about choices and decide which one is the best to make (Review 4)
evaporation	the process in which a liquid changes into a gas (Review 10)
evidence	observations and measurements connected to a problem (Review 4)
experiment	a carefully planned activity done to help answer a question, test a hypothesis, or support an opinion (Review 1)
extinct	no longer existing as a species (Review 15)
flower	the part of a plant extending from the stem that helps the plant reproduce (Review 14)
food chain	the link from a lower organism (a plant, for example) to a higher organism (a rabbit) to a higher organism (a fox), and so on; it is a direct path from bottom to top (Review 19)
food group	a classification of food that is based on the most important kinds of nutrients it contains; examples include the fruit group and the dairy group (Review 17)
food guide pyramid	a chart in the shape of a pyramid that shows what kinds of food groups there are and how much of each group we should eat every day (Review 17)
food web	a combination of food chains showing how different living things must balance each other in nature; also called "web of life" (Review 19)
force	a push or pull that causes something to change its speed or direction (Review 7)
forecast	to predict the weather; a weather prediction (Review 10)
friction	a force that causes two things to slow down and heat up when they rub against each other (Review 7)
fulcrum	the supporting point on which a balance rests (Review 8)

gas	matter that does not have a definite shape or volume (Review 5)
gene	a piece of information that controls one trait of an organism; located inside an organism's cells (Review 15)
genetic information	information that tells cells what kind of cell to be and that controls which traits offspring receive from the parents (Review 15)
germination	when the seeds of a plant sprout (Review 14)
graph	a way of representing numbers in picture form (Review 3)
gravity	a force that pulls two objects toward each other (Review 7)
health habit	something that a person does regularly and that helps or hurts the body (Review 17)
herbivore	an animal that eats only plants (Review 20)
high pressure area	an area of the atmosphere that generally has clear skies and whose air moves in a clockwise direction (Review 10)
humidity	the amount of water vapor in the air (Review 10)
hypothesis	a reasonable guess or possible explanation that can be tested (Review 1)
igneous rock	a rock, such as granite, that is formed by the cooling and hardening of magma (Review 11)
inquiry	an examination, exploration, or investigation designed to solve a problem or answer a question (Review 1)
insect	a small invertebrate animal with a segmented body and an exoskeleton (such as a beetle, grasshopper, or mosquito) (Review 12)
instinct	something that an organism is born knowing how to do (Review 15)
instrument	a special tool used to make observations or measure things (Review 2)
invertebrate	an animal that does not have a backbone (Review 12)

judgment	an opinion about what the best action or answer is (Review 4)
lava	liquid rock that has risen to the surface of the earth, often because of a volcanic eruption (Review 11)
leaf	the part of the plant that uses sunshine to make food for the plant (Review 14)
learned	having been taught to do something, often by a parent (Review 15)
lever	an unbending object that rotates around a fulcrum (Review 8)
life cycle	a pattern of living things that involves birth, growth, reproduction, and death (Review 14)
line graph	a picture showing how data changes over time (Review 3)
liquid	matter that has a definite volume but not a definite shape (Review 5)
living	being alive or showing signs of life; living things have cells, need food and water, grow, reproduce, and respond to changes in the environment (Review 12)
low pressure area	an area of the atmosphere that generally has cloudy skies and whose air moves in a counterclockwise direction (Review 10)
machine	anything that helps you do work with less force or with greater speed (Review 8)
magma	molten or liquid rock (Review 11)
mammal	a warm-blooded animal that has hair, gives birth to live young, and feeds milk to its young (Review 12)
matter	material from which all substances are made (Review 5)
mechanical energy	the energy of motion and of the position of things (Review 6)
metamorphic rock	a rock, such as marble, that is formed when large amounts of heat and pressure are applied to other rocks (Review 11)

metamorphosis	the special stages some organisms go through to become an adult from an egg (Review 15)
meteorologist	a scientist who studies weather (Review 10)
mineral	a nonliving, solid material that is formed in nature and made of crystals; rocks are made of minerals (Review 11)
molecule	a tiny unit of matter, made up of atoms joined together (Review 5)
natural resource	something found in nature that humans use (Review 21)
nonliving	never having been alive (Review 12)
nonrenewable resource	a resource that cannot be replaced by nature (Review 20)
nutrient	a substance, such as vitamins, minerals, or water, needed for the healthy growth of living things (Review 17)
observation	the information gathered from noticing what your senses tell you (Review 2)
offspring	the product of reproduction; the new organisms created by the parent organisms (Review 15)
omnivore	an animal that is both a carnivore and a herbivore—an animal that eats both plants and animals (Review 20)
orbit	the path of an object in space as it travels around another object (Review 9)
organism	a living being (Review 12)
phase	the different shapes of the moon as it progresses through a one-month cycle, as seen from Earth (Review 9)
photosynthesis	the process by which plants make food from sunlight, water, and carbon dioxide (Review 14)
physical change	a change in the appearance, size, shape, or state of matter (Review 5)
physical property	a feature of matter that can be observed without changing the kind of matter it is (Review 5)
pollution	any harmful thing that causes the environment to be unhealthy (Review 21)

precipitation	a form of water that falls from the clouds to the earth; depending on the temperature, the water can be in the form of rain, hail, snow, and so on (Review 10)
precision	when measurements or observations are accurate (Review 2)
predator	an animal that eats other animals (Review 19)
prey	an animal that is eaten by other animals (Review 19)
producer	an organism that changes the sun's energy into food for primary consumers; plants (Review 20)
protein	a type of molecule that helps build our bodies (Review 18)
recycle	to reuse materials in the environment (Review 20)
renewable resource	a resource that can be replaced by nature (Review 20)
reproduce	the process by which organisms create offspring and begin a new generation (Review 14)
revolution	the movement of an object around another object; for example, it takes Earth one year to make one revolution around the sun (Review 9)
rock cycle	the long process of heating, cooling, compressing, and breaking down the minerals that make up rocks (Review 11)
root	the part of the plant below ground that collects minerals and water and holds the plant in the soil (Review 14)
rotation	the spin of something on its axis; for example, it takes the earth one day to make one rotation (Review 9)
scientific method	an orderly way to learn about nature; a scientist first has an idea about how to answer a question, then collects data to see if that idea is correct (Review 1)
sedimentary rock	rock formed by earth materials that have been deposited by wind, water, or ice (Review 11)

sense	one of the ways in which an organism experiences the world: sight, hearing, touch, taste, or smell (Review 2)
shelter	protection against harmful things in the environment (Review 13)
solid	matter that has both a definite volume and shape (Review 5)
species	a group of organisms sharing a set of characteristics and a specific group name (Review 12)
state of matter	the way particles of matter are arranged to form a solid, liquid, or gas (Review 5)
stem	the supporting part of the plant that carries the minerals and water to the leaves (Review 14)
technology	anything that someone makes to help do something or to solve a problem (Review 21)
trait	a feature that an organism inherits from its parents (Review 15)
transform	to change from one form of energy to another (Review 6)
variable	a factor that changes in an experiment (Review 1)
variation	the differences within a species that help the species survive (Review 15)
vertebrate	an animal that has a backbone (Review 12)
volume	the amount of space that something takes up (Review 5)
water cycle	a continuous movement of water from the ground to the air and back to the ground (Review 10)
water vapor	water in gas form (Review 10)
weather	atmospheric conditions at any point in time (Review 10)
weathering	when materials such as rock are broken down by things in nature such as wind and water (Review 11)
work	the use of energy to create a force to move an object (Review 8)

On the Web

We hope you are interested in finding out more about the science topics in this book. If you like to "surf" the Internet, the following list of Internet addresses is designed to help you explore science topics on computers at home or school. The addresses are current at the time of publication but may not be available at a later date. In addition to these websites, there are many, many more places to learn about science; these are just places to start. Happy surfing!

All About Meteorology

http://www.weather.com/learn_more/meteorologist.html#educational

Learn how to become an amateur meteorologist through a little reading and some backyard observing—includes information on recording temperature and atmospheric pressure, measuring moisture, and recording winds.

Amazing Space: Education Online from the Hubble Space Telescope

http://oposite.stsci.edu/pubinfo/education/amazing-space/

Includes a variety of web-based activities for the classroom, such as building the Milky Way or planning a mission to service the Hubble Space Telescope.

Ask Dr. Universe

http://www.wsu.edu/DrUniverse/

A question and answer site with detailed and easy-to-understand responses. Search for information by keyword, read a new question and answer every day, or send in your own questions.

Bill Nye the Science Guy

http://www.disney.go.com/DisneyTelevision/BillNye/

An offshoot of Bill Nye's TV show about science for kids— contains a guide to every episode, plus fun facts and experiments on a variety of topics.

Cells Alive

http://www.cellsalive.com

See this site for information on penicillin, parasites, dust mites, and more—includes videos of cell processes.

Come to Your Senses

http://tqjunior.advanced.org/3750/

Includes an article, quiz, and list of interesting facts on each of the five senses, plus a glossary of sense words.

The Cub Den

http://www.nature-net.com/bears/cubden.html

Read "amazing facts about bears," current bear news, and a list of recommended books on bears for kids.

Dan's Wild Wild Weather Page

http://www.whnt19.com/kidwx/

A site designed for kids 6-16 years of age by a TV news station meteorologist. Learn about El Niño, tornadoes, hurricanes, and more.

Discovery Online

http://www.discovery.com

This site has all sorts of interesting articles on things such as dinosaurs, whether animals have emotions, and why pizza makes you thirsty. Some articles have videos, games, and/or activities, too.

The Electronic Zoo

http://netvet.wustl.edu/e-zoo.htm

A great collection of Internet animal resources. Includes information on veterinary science, ecology, and just about every kind of animal.

Energy Education from the California Energy Commission

http://www.energy.ca.gov/education

Includes science projects for kids, tips for kids to help the environment, biographies about famous scientists, games, puzzles, and more.

Exploring Planets in the Classroom

http://www.soest.hawaii.edu/SPACEGRANT/class_acts/

This site includes more than 25 hands-on activities exploring space science, geology, the earth, and the planets.

The Nine Planets

http://seds.lpl.arizona.edu/billa/tnp/

Learn about the history, myths, and current scientific knowledge of each of the planets and moons in our solar system. Includes pictures from NASA spacecraft. Some pages have sounds and movies.

Star Child

http://starchild.gsfc.nasa.gov

Provides information and activities about the sun, the moon, the planets, comets, asteroids, and more.

The Why Files

http://whyfiles.news.wisc.edu

Find stories that explore the science behind the news. New stories are featured twice a month on topics including mad cow disease, why people crave chocolate, and why the house cat is a major urban predator.

You Can with Beakman and Jax

http://www.youcan.com

Lists a wide range of questions and answers that show how science is part of everyday life. Learn how a remote control works, why feet smell, and why leaves change color in the fall.

Test-Taking Tips

Sometimes when you take a test, you don't know all of the answers. One way to get a better score is to study the material that's being tested. But even knowing the material may not be enough if you don't feel comfortable taking tests. That's where a little test preparation can help you.

Most people don't know *everything* there is to know about a subject, but they often know *something* about it. Studying will help you learn new information. Test preparation will help you make better use of the information you learn. Both are important.

Taking Apart a Multiple-Choice Question

- Multiple-choice test **items** (problems) are made up of a **stem** (usually a question) and several **responses** (sometimes called **answer choices** or **foils**).

- Only one of the answer choices is the **key** (the best answer).

- The other answer choices are supposed to look good to a person who doesn't know everything he or she should about the material.

In the following **item**, circle the **stem** once and the **responses** twice. Underline the **key**.

1. Giraffes belong to which of the following groups?
   A. fish
   B. reptile
   C. bird
   D. mammal

Choosing the Correct Answer

By learning how to get rid of choices that you know are wrong, you'll increase your chances of choosing the correct answer and raising your score on the test.

Imagine for a moment that you have just read a multiple-choice test item that has four answer choices. It looks something like this:

2. Kjfzklf jklas jrljawk l34jlk 3ujoi?
   A. jkfjkjeiosr   C. omelrj
   B. jies   D. 324u4i

Whoa! How are you going to answer that one? You haven't even got a clue what the question is, let alone what any of the answer choices mean.

There's only one way. You've got to guess. Hmmmm . . . if you guess, what are your chances of choosing the correct answer?

The chances aren't too great—you only have a 1-in-4, or 25 percent, chance of guessing right. Not good enough to pass the test, if all the items are as hard as this one.

ZAP® the Obvious Wrong Choices

Instead of blind guessing, you need to learn to "Zero-in-And-Pick"—*ZAP*— before you guess.

Look at the next example:

3. Which of the following types of animals is able to fly?
   A. *Chiroptera*
   B. *Panthera tigris*
   C. *Proboscidea*
   D. *Perissodactyla*

Another tough one. Do you recognize any of the answer choices?

How about **B**? Even if you aren't totally sure, you might take a guess that *Panthera tigris* is some kind of a cat since the word "tigris" looks sort of like "tiger." In fact, *Panthera tigris* is the scientific name for the Bengal tiger, an animal that can make some pretty huge leaps but has never been known to fly. You can *ZAP* **B**.

Okay, so you've *ZAPPED* one answer choice. Your chances have just gotten better. Now you have a one-in-three chance of choosing the correct answer. Increasing your chances on a single item may not seem like a big deal, but increasing your chances on the entire test may make the difference between passing and failing.

Now that you know that *ZAPPING* can help you get a better score, let's zero in on using it for multiple-choice tests.

Getting the Best of a Multiple-Choice Test Item

TIP 1: Read the stem carefully.

In a well-written test item, the stem will ask you to do something specific—it will give you a job or a task. For example:

4. Rocks are classified by the way they are formed. Which of the following groups contains rocks that are formed by volcanoes?
   A. igneous
   B. marble
   C. gypsum
   D. sedimentary

Think about it:

What's the **task** in the item above? To find out which of the listed groups contains rocks formed by volcanoes.

The stem asks for a **group** of rocks. The groups of rock formation are igneous, sedimentary, and metamorphic.

Neither marble nor gypsum is a group of rocks, so *ZAP* **B** and **C**. You've just narrowed the answer choices down to two. Now, your chances of guessing correctly are 1 in 2 instead of 1 in 4.

TIP 2: Read the stem as many times as you need to until you understand the task, or what you are supposed to do.

You may need to read it more than once, but don't spend all morning on the same stem. If you can't understand it after two or three readings, you're probably better off going on to the rest of the test. The lightbulb in your head may start to glow after you turn the page. You can always go back to answer the question later.

TIP 3: Read all responses before making a final choice.

This will help you *ZAP* responses that are only partly correct. For example:

5. Which of the following is not a part of a living plant?
    A. roots
    B. leaves
    C. heart
    D. stems

Think about it:

The task is to identify the answer that is not part of a living plant. By reading all the answers carefully, you know plants have roots (A), leaves (B), and stems (D). People and animals have hearts, but not plants.

TIP 4: Narrow your choices by *ZAPPING* the responses you know are wrong.

When there are two opposite responses, *ZAP* the one that is least likely to be correct. This will give you fewer choices. For example:

6. Why is it colder in the United States in the winter than in the summer?
    A. The sun is hotter during the winter.
    B. The sun is colder during the winter.
    C. The Northern Hemisphere is tilted toward the sun.
    D. The Northern Hemisphere is tilted away from the sun.

Think about it:

What's the task? To decide why it is colder in the United States in the winter than in the summer.

There are two pairs of opposite answer choices. What a break! In each pair, *ZAP* the opposite that makes the least sense. The United States is in the Northern Hemisphere (the top half of the earth), so if the Northern Hemisphere were tilted toward the sun, it would be hotter, not colder, in the winter. And if the sun were hotter during the winter, again, it would be hot, not cold. *ZAP* **A** and **C**.

Now, make a choice from the two responses that are left.

Which do you choose?

TIP 5: Once you decide that a response is wrong, do not look at it again.

Cross off the letter of any responses that you have *ZAPPED*. If you can't decide between the ones left over and have to come back to the question later, you won't waste time thinking about the same things over again.

TIP 6: If no response can be *ZAPPED*, do not guess right away.

Mark an X next to the item and go on. Sometimes the correct answer will come to you while you are thinking about something else. Go back to it later.

TIP 7: Do not leave any blanks.

Other than not getting any points for wrong answers, your score will not be hurt by wrong answers. But don't just blindly guess until after you have followed all the tips above.

New York State Learning Standards for Scientific Inquiry and Elementary Science

Blast Off on New York Science, Book 4, is based on the Scientific Inquiry and Elementary Science portions of the *New York State Learning Standards for Mathematics, Science, and Technology.* The workbook is designed to prepare students for the Elementary Science Program Evaluation Test (ESPET). The following table matches the standards to the *Blast Off* reviews and activities in which they are addressed.

Standard 1: Analysis, Inquiry, and Design

Scientific Inquiry	
Key Ideas	***Blast Off*** **Reviews and Activities**
1. The central purpose of scientific inquiry is to develop explanations of natural phenomena in a continuing, creative process. Students: • ask "why" questions in attempts to seek greater understanding concerning objects and events they have observed and heard about. • question the explanations they hear from others and read about, seeking clarification and comparing them with their own observations and understandings. • develop relationships among observations to construct descriptions of objects and events and to form their own tentative explanations of what they have observed.	Reviews 1, 4 Activities 1, 3

Standard 1: Analysis, Inquiry, and Design

Scientific Inquiry	
Key Ideas	***Blast Off*** **Reviews and Activities**
2. Beyond the use of reasoning and consensus, scientific inquiry involves the testing of proposed explanations involving the use of conventional techniques and procedures and usually requiring considerable ingenuity. Students: • develop written plans for exploring phenomena or for evaluating explanations guided by questions or proposed explanations they have helped formulate. • share their research plans with others and revise them based on their suggestions. • carry out their plans for exploring phenomena through direct observation and through the use of simple instruments that permit measurements of quantities (e.g., length, mass, volume, temperature, and time).	Reviews 1, 2 Activities 1, 2
3. The observations made while testing proposed explanations, when analyzed using conventional and invented methods, provide new insights into phenomena. Students: • organize observations and measurements of objects and events through classification and the preparation of simple charts and tables. • interpret organized observations and measurements, recognizing simple patterns, sequences and relationships. • share their findings with others and actively seek their interpretations and ideas. • adjust their explanations and understandings of objects and events based on their findings and new ideas.	Reviews 2, 3 Activities 2, 3

Standard 4: Elementary Science

Physical Setting	
Key Ideas	***Blast Off* Reviews and Activities**
1. The Earth and celestial phenomena can be described by principles of relative motion and perspective. Students: • describe patterns of daily, monthly, and seasonal changes in their environment.	Reviews 9, 10 Activity 7
2. Many of the phenomena that we observe on Earth involve interactions among components of air, water, and land. Students: • describe the relationships among air, water, and land on Earth.	Reviews 10, 11
3. Matter is made up of particles whose properties determine the observable characteristics of matter and its reactivity. Students: • observe and describe properties of materials using appropriate tools. • describe chemical and physical changes, including changes in states of matter.	Reviews 2, 5 Activities 2, 4
4. Energy exists in many forms, and when these forms change energy is conserved. Students: • describe a variety of forms of energy (e.g., heat, chemical, light) and the changes that occur in objects when they interact with those forms of energy. • observe the way one form of energy can be transformed into another form of energy present in common situations (e.g., mechanical to heat energy, mechanical to electrical energy, chemical to heat energy).	Review 6 Activity 5
5. Energy and matter interact through forces that result in changes in motion. Students: • describe the effects of common forces (pushes and pulls) on objects, such as those caused by gravity, magnetism, and mechanical forces. • describe how forces can operate across distances.	Reviews 7, 8 Activity 6

Standard 4: Elementary Science

The Living Environment	
Key Ideas	*Blast Off* **Reviews and Activities**
1. Living things are both similar to and different from each other and nonliving things. Students: • describe the characteristics of and variations between living and nonliving things. • describe the life processes common to all living things.	Reviews 12, 13 Activity 8
2. Organisms inherit genetic information in a variety of ways that result in continuity of structure and function between parents and offspring. Students: • recognize that traits of living things are both inherited and acquired or learned. • recognize that for humans and other living things there is genetic continuity between generations.	Review 15 Activity 9
3. Individual organisms and species change over time. Students: • describe how the structures of plants and animals complement the environment of the plant or animal. • observe that differences within a species may give individuals an advantage in surviving and reproducing.	Reviews 15, 16 Activity 10
4. The continuity of life is sustained through reproduction and development. Students: • describe the major stages in the life cycles of selected plants and animals. • describe evidence of growth, repair, and maintenance, such as nails, hair, and bone, and the healing of cuts and bruises.	Reviews 14, 15, 18

Standard 4: Elementary Science

The Living Environment	
Key Ideas	***Blast Off*** **Reviews and Activities**
5. Organisms maintain a dynamic equilibrium that sustains life. Students: • describe basic life functions of common living specimens (guppy, mealworm, gerbil). • describe some survival behaviors of common living specimens. • describe the factors that help promote good health and growth in humans.	Reviews 13, 17
6. Plants and animals depend on each other and their physical environment. Students: • describe how plants and animals, including humans, depend upon each other and the nonliving environment. • describe the relationship of the sun as an energy source for living and nonliving cycles.	Reviews 6, 19, 20 Activity 11
7. Human decisions and activities have had a profound impact on the physical and living environment. Students: • identify ways in which humans have changed their environment and the effects of those changes.	Review 21 Activity 12